Personal Tax

(Finance Act 2016)

Workbook

for assessments from January 2017

Aubrey Penning
Bob Thomas

Published by Osborne Books Limited
Tel 01905 748071
Email books@osbornebooks.co.uk
Website www.osbornebooks.co.uk

Design by Laura Ingham

Printed by CPI Group (UK) Limited, Croydon, CR0 4YY, on environmentally friendly, acid-free paper from managed forests.

MIX
Paper from
responsible sources
FSC® C019777

British Library Cataloguing in Publication Data
A catalogue record for this book is available from the British Library

ISBN 978 1909173 958

Contents

Introduction

Chapter activities

Answers to chapter activities

Practice assessments

Answers to practice assessments

AAT Reference Material

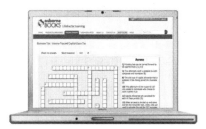

Introduction

Qualifications covered

This book has been written specifically to cover the Unit 'Personal Tax' which is an optional Unit for the following qualifications:

AAT Professional Diploma in Accounting – Level 4

AAT Professional Diploma in Accounting at SCQF – Level 8

This book contains Chapter Activities which provide extra practice material in addition to the activities included in the Osborne Books Tutorial text, and Practice Assessments to prepare the student for the computer based assessments. The latter are based directly on the structure, style and content of the sample assessment material provided by the AAT at www.aat.org.uk.

Suggested answers to the Chapter Activities and Practice Assessments are set out in this book.

Osborne Study and Revision Materials

The materials featured on the previous page are tailored to the needs of students studying this Unit and revising for the assessment. They include:

■ **Tutorials:** paperback books with practice activities
■ **Student Zone:** access to Osborne Books online resources
■ **Osborne Books App:** Osborne Books ebooks for mobiles and tablets

Visit www.osbornebooks.co.uk for details of study and revision resources and access to online material.

Exams, Finance Acts and tax years

This book has been designed to include guidance and exercises based on Tax Year 2016/17 (Finance Act 2016). We understand that the AAT plan to assess this legislation from 1 January 2017 to 31 December 2017. Tutors and students are advised to check this with the AAT and ensure that they sit the correct computer based assessment.

Chapter activities

1 Introduction to income tax

1.1 State whether each of the following statements is true or false.

		True	False
(a)	Different tax systems are based on different views of which are the most important tax principles and how they should be applied		
(b)	The principle of equity means that every taxpayer should pay the same amount of tax, regardless of their circumstances		
(c)	Vertical equity means that taxation is fair at different levels in society		
(d)	Although tax is often used in an attempt to change behaviour, this conflicts with the principle of neutrality		
(e)	A progressive tax system is one in which the same proportion of income is paid in tax for all income levels		
(f)	A tax system that charges every taxpayer the same percentage of their income in tax is a proportional system		

1.2 State whether each of the following statements is true or false.

		True	False
(a)	It is not the taxpayer's responsibility to inform HMRC of any untaxed taxable income, unless they have been asked to complete a tax return		
(b)	Accountants must normally follow the rules of confidentiality, but there are exceptions		
(c)	Where a practitioner has knowledge or suspicion that his client is money laundering, then he has a duty to inform the relevant person or authority		
(d)	Accountants should warn clients if they suspect money laundering to give the client a chance to cease the activity		
(e)	When an accountant is advising a client the greatest duty of care is to the client		

1.3   State which of the following can provide sources of information about tax law and its interpretation.

		Yes	No
(a)	HMRC extra-statutory concessions		
(b)	Statute law		
(c)	HMRC statements of practice		
(d)	Case law		
(e)	Website www.gov.uk		
(f)	HMRC guides and help sheets		

1.4   Match the following examples of income with the correct income category.

Sample Income
UK dividends
Partnership profits
Rents from land
Earnings from a job

Income Category
Property Income
Savings and Investment Income
Trading Income
Employment, Pension and Social Security Income

1.5   Tick the columns to show which of the following categories of income is taxed on an accruals basis, and which is on a receipts basis (ie based on when received).

Income Category	Accruals basis	Receipts basis
(a) Property Income		
(b) Savings and Investment Income		
(c) Trading Income		
(d) Employment, Pension and Social Security Income		

1.6   State which of the following types of income are exempt from income tax.

Income Category	Exempt	Not exempt
(a) Employment income		
(b) Income from an ISA		
(c) Premium bond prizes		
(d) Rent received from a buy-to-let property		
(e) Betting winnings (unless a professional gambler)		
(f) Lottery prizes		

1.7 Analyse the following list of statements by ticking the appropriate column.

Statement	True	False
(a) UK residence is determined by some specific tests that are applied to the individual for each tax year		
(b) An individual who lives permanently in the UK can choose the domicile of any country in the world, simply by completing the relevant form		
(c) An individual who is resident and domiciled in the UK will pay UK tax on their worldwide income and gains		
(d) An individual who is resident in the UK, but not UK domiciled will pay UK tax on income and gains arising in the UK		
(e) An individual who is resident in the UK, but not UK domiciled will never pay UK tax on income and gains arising in the rest of the world		
(f) An individual who is resident in the UK, but not UK domiciled can elect to pay UK tax on their overseas income on a remittance basis, but there is normally a substantial charge for this basis to apply		

2 Income from property

2.1 Chester has two properties in addition to his home, details of which are as follows:

Two bedroom house:

(1) This unfurnished house is rented out for £850 per month. The property was occupied this tax year until 1 February when the tenants suddenly moved out, owing the rent for January. Chester knows that he will not recover this rent. The property was let again from 1 May to another family.

(2) Chester had to pay £530 for redecoration in March following the poor condition of the property at that time.

(3) The only other expense paid by Chester on the house was 10% management charge to the agent on rent received.

One bedroom flat:

(1) This furnished flat is rented out for £550 per month. The property was rented all tax year.

(2) Chester paid council tax and water rates on the flat, totalling £1,100 for the period that the flat was occupied. He also paid buildings and contents insurance of £340 for the year.

Calculate the profit or loss made on each property, using the following table.

	Two bedroom house £	One bedroom flat £
Income		
Expenses:		

2.2 Stephan rents out one furnished property. The following is a statement compiled from his accounting records relating to the tax year.

	£	£
Rental Income Receivable		12,000
less expenditure:		
Council Tax	700	
Water Rates	300	
Insurance	380	
Cost of replacement furniture	2,100	
Depreciation of furniture	800	
Managing Agent's Charges	1,200	
		5,480
Profit		6,520

Required:

Calculate the assessable property income for Stephan, using the following table.

	£	£
Income		
Expenditure:		
Assessable Income		

2.3 The following list of expenditure relates to a rental property.

Analyse the expenditure according to its tax treatment.

Expenditure	Allowable	Not allowable
(a) Replacement of washing machine		
(b) Legal fees relating to purchase of property		
(c) Cleaning property between tenancies		
(d) Legal fees relating to tenancy agreement		
(e) Renovation of property between purchase and first tenancy		
(f) Insurance against non-recoverable rent		

2.4 The following expenditure was incurred during a void period between tenancies.

Analyse the expenditure according to its tax treatment.

Expenditure	Allowable	Not allowable
(a) Internal redecoration		
(b) Replacement of carpets		
(c) Mortgage interest		
(d) Property insurance		
(e) Mortgage repayments of capital		
(f) Advertising for tenants		

3 Income from savings and investments

3.1 Analyse the following statements into those that are true and those that are false.

		True	False
(a)	The 0% starting rate for savings income will only apply if taxable general income is less than £5,000		
(b)	There is no dividend allowance available for additional rate taxpayers		
(c)	An individual whose only income (before deducting the personal allowance) is savings income of £15,000 will pay no income tax		
(d)	Income that falls within the personal savings allowance will still be treated as using up the tax bands and can result in savings or dividend income being pushed into a higher tax band		
(e)	There is no personal savings allowance available for additional rate taxpayers		
(f)	The personal savings allowance can be used to save tax on savings income or dividend income		

3.2 An individual has the following income before deduction of the personal allowance:

General Income   £12,000

Savings Income   £1,500

Dividend Income   £2,000

Calculate the amount of income tax payable on each of these categories of income, and in total.

3.3 An individual has the following income before deduction of the personal allowance:

General Income   £15,000

Savings Income   £2,500

Dividend Income   £6,000

Calculate the amount of income tax payable on each of these categories of income, and in total.

3.4 An individual has the following income before deduction of the personal allowance:

General Income   £10,000

Savings Income   £7,500

Dividend Income   £5,000

Calculate the amount of income tax payable on each of these categories of income, and in total.

3.5 The following statements relate to Individual Savings Accounts (ISAs). Identify which statements are true and which are false.

	True	False
(a) Cash ISAs can only be opened by individuals aged 18 or over who are UK resident		
(b) Stocks and shares ISAs can be used for shares in listed companies and government securities (gilts)		
(c) The interest and / or dividends received from investment in ISAs are tax free and do not utilise the personal savings allowance or dividend allowance		
(d) Each individual can only invest in one cash ISA and one stocks and shares ISA in a tax year		
(e) Cash ISAs can only be transferred to another provider at the end of a tax year		
(f) ISAs cannot be held in joint names, and individual investors must be UK resident		

4 Income from employment

4.1 Complete the following table by correctly matching the indicators as relating to employment or self employment.

Indicators of Employment	Indicators of Self Employment

Indicators

- Choose work hours and invoice for work done
- Need to do the work yourself
- Told how, where and when to do work
- No risk of capital or losses
- Work for several people or organisations
- Decide yourself how, when and where to do work
- Can employ helper or substitute
- Employer provides equipment
- Risk own capital and bear losses from work that is not to standard
- Work set hours and paid regular wage with sick pay and holidays
- Usually work for one employer
- Provide own equipment

4.2   **(a)**   What scale charge percentage would be applied for petrol cars with the following CO_2 emissions?

       (1)   44 g/km

       (2)   134 g/km

       (3)   151 g/km

       (4)   249 g/km

  (b)   Silvia was provided with a secondhand car on 6 October 2016. It cost the company £8,000, but the list price of this car when bought new was £17,000. The car has a CO_2 emission of 168 g/km, and has a diesel engine. The company pays for all running costs, except private fuel.

       (1)   The cost of the car used in the benefit in kind computation is

       £ [   ]

       (2)   The percentage used in the benefit in kind computation is

       [   ] %

       (3)   The assessable benefit for Silvia relating to the car for 2016/17 is

       £ [   ]

4.3   **(a)**   When accommodation is purchased by an employer, what is the value of the property above which an additional benefit is applied?

(a)	£60,000	
(b)	£70,000	
(c)	£75,000	
(d)	£80,000	
(e)	£100,000	
(f)	£125,000	

  (b)   Would the following situations be treated as being job-related where no accommodation benefit arises?

		Yes	No
(a)	House provided for a vicar		
(b)	House provided by employer for accountant working for a housing association		
(c)	Flat in sheltered accommodation provided for an on-site care manager		

(c) Summer was provided with accommodation in the form of a flat that the employer purchased recently for £165,000. It is not job related. The flat has an annual value of £9,300. Summer pays £200 per month towards the private use of the flat. Assume that the HMRC official interest rate is 3.00%. Her taxable benefit is:

(a)	£6,900	
(b)	£9,300	
(c)	£9,600	
(d)	£12,000	

4.4 On 6 December 2016, Kevin was provided with a company loan of £16,000 on which he pays interest at 1.5% per annum. On 6 February 2017 Kevin repaid £2,000. The official rate of interest is 3.00%.

What is the benefit in kind for 2016/17 to the nearest £?

4.5   **(a)**   Dee uses her own car for business travelling. During the tax year she travelled 11,500 business miles for which she was paid 50p per mile by her employer. The impact of this is:

(a)	She will have a taxable amount of £575	
(b)	She will have a taxable amount of £875	
(c)	She will claim an allowable expense of £875	
(d)	She will claim an allowable expense of £575	

(b)   Eddie has an occupational pension scheme to which he contributes 5% of his salary. His employer contributes 6% of his salary. His salary was £28,400. The impact of this is:

(a)	His taxable salary will be increased by £1,704	
(b)	His taxable salary will be reduced by £1,420	
(c)	His taxable salary will be increased by £284	
(d)	His basic rate band will be extended by £1,775	

(c)   Steve pays £300 per year in subscriptions to professional bodies. His employer reimburses him £180. The overall impact of this is:

(a)	No impact on tax	
(b)	An allowable deduction of £120	
(c)	A benefit of £180	
(d)	An allowable deduction of £300	

(d)   Genna has a non-contributory occupational pension scheme. This means:

(a)	The employer pays a percentage of her salary into the scheme, but Genna does not	
(b)	Genna pays a percentage of her salary into the scheme, but the employer does not	
(c)	Only the Government pays a percentage of her salary into the scheme	
(d)	Genna and the Government both pay a percentage of her salary into the scheme	

5 Preparing income tax computations

5.1 John has the following income for the tax year:

Employment income	£47,500
Rental income	£10,350
Bank account interest	£700
Dividends	£6,500

John paid £3,200 (net) into a private pension scheme, and made gift aid payments totalling £1,600 (net).

Using the following table, calculate the total Income Tax liability for John.

	£
Employment income	
Rental income	
Savings income	
Dividend income	
Less Personal Allowance	
Taxable income	
Tax Calculation:	

5.2 Dave and Sue are a married couple with a joint savings account that produces annual savings income of £4,000. They have no other savings income.

Dave has general income of £20,000, and Sue has general income of £55,000.

Complete the following table to show for each person, the annual Income Tax on the savings income only based on three alternative situations:

- The current situation
- If all the savings were held in Dave's name
- If all the savings were held in Sue's name

Situation	Dave's tax on savings income £	Sue's tax on savings income £
Current position		
All savings in Dave's name		
All savings in Sue's name		

5.3 Karen has employment income of £40,000, plus normal profits from a rental property of £8,000 per year. She is considering whether to spend an additional £6,000 on replacement carpets and curtains for the rental property.

Complete the following table.

	Normal situation £	Replacing carpet and curtains £
Taxable Income		
Tax at 20%		
Tax at 40%		
Total Income Tax		
Net Cost of Replacements		

5.4 Wayne earns £45,000 per year from his job as a Sales Manager, and is entitled to a diesel company car and all fuel (business and private). The car has a list price of £22,000, but was purchased at a discount for £19,500. It has emissions of 159 g/km.

Wayne makes cash contributions of £1,600 per year into a personal pension scheme.

Calculate Wayne's tax liability (to the nearest £), using the following table.

Workings:	
	£
Salary	
Car benefit	
Fuel benefit	
Personal allowance	
Taxable income	
Tax at 20%:	
Tax at 40%:	
Total tax liability	

5.5   Rachel had employment income of £91,500 and received dividends of £17,500. She paid £1,200 (net) into a personal pension scheme.

Calculate her total income tax liability (ie before deduction of tax paid) for the tax year, using the table given below.

	£
Employment Income	
Dividends	
Personal allowance	
Taxable income	

6 Capital gains tax

6.1 For each statement, tick the appropriate box.

		Actual proceeds used	Deemed proceeds used	No gain or loss basis
(a)	Father gives an asset to his son			
(b)	Wife sells an asset to her husband			
(c)	Simon gives an asset to his friend			
(d)	Margaret sells an asset to her cousin for £15,000 when the market value is £40,000			
(e)	Brian gives an asset to his civil partner, Dave			

6.2 Alex bought an asset in January 2008 for £36,000, selling it in the tax year for £35,000. He paid auctioneer's commission of 4% when he bought the asset and 5% when he sold the asset.

The loss on this asset is:

(a)	£nil	
(b)	£1,000	
(c)	£4,190	
(d)	£2,440	

Legal fees are an allowable deduction where they relate to the purchase or sale of an asset.

TRUE / FALSE

6.3 State whether each of the following statements is true or false:

		True	False
(a)	The annual exemption is applied after capital losses are deducted		
(b)	Capital losses from the same year cannot safeguard the annual exemption		
(c)	Capital gains on residential property are taxed at 28% for higher rate tax payers		
(d)	Capital losses can be set against gains of the previous tax year		
(e)	Capital losses brought forward can safeguard the annual exemption when offset against current year gains		

6.4 Josie has a capital loss brought forward of £4,000. She is a higher rate income tax payer.

She sold an asset during the tax year for £19,000. She had been given the asset by her husband when it was worth £8,000. Her husband originally paid £6,500 for the asset.

Complete the following sentences:

(a) The gain on the asset is £ _____

(b) The amount of loss that will be relieved is £ _____

(c) The capital gains tax payable is £ _____

(d) The loss to be carried forward to the next tax year is £ _____

6.5 Complete the following table to show which assets are exempt from capital gains tax and which are chargeable.

Asset	Exempt	Chargeable
Antique furniture valued at £30,000		
Principal private residence		
Clock		
Shares		
Holiday home		
Government securities		
Vintage car		
Land		

6.6 Richard bought a house on 1 January 2000 for £125,000. He lived in the house until 31 December 2002 when he moved abroad for one year to work. He returned from abroad on 31 December 2003, and then immediately moved into his elderly father's house until 30 June 2005, leaving his own home empty. He then moved back into his own house until 31 December 2012, when he moved to a new home and put the house on the market. The house was eventually sold on 1 January 2017 for £205,000.

(a) Which periods are treated as occupied and which are not?

Occupation / Deemed Occupation	Non-occupation

(b) What is the chargeable gain on the property?

£

6.7 The following table relates to sales of chattels.

Match the statements shown below to the correct asset details.

Asset	Sale proceeds	Cost	Statement
1	£4,000	£7,000	
2	£14,000	£8,000	
3	£8,000	£3,000	
4	£3,000	£5,000	
5	£15,000	£21,000	

Statements:

- Exempt asset
- Calculate gain as normal
- Calculate loss as normal
- Sale proceeds to be £6,000
- Chattel marginal relief applies

6.8 Paul bought 20,000 shares in Lincoln Ltd for £5 per share in October 2000. He received a bonus issue of 1 for 25 shares in March 2003. In January 2017, Paul sold 8,000 shares for £9 per share.

Clearly showing the balance of shares, and their value, to carry forward, calculate the gain made on these shares. All workings must be shown in your calculations.

7 Inheritance tax

7.1 Elizabeth died, leaving an estate of £750,000. She had not made any lifetime transfers. In her will she left the following:

- £250,000 to her husband, Phil

- £5,000 to charity

The balance of her estate to her son, Robert

Calculate the Inheritance Tax due on the estate, and how much Robert will receive.

7.2 Paul and Mary had been married for several years, when Mary died. Mary had not made any lifetime transfers. Mary left £40,000 to each of their two sons and the balance to Paul. Mary's estate was valued at £350,000.

Three years after Mary's death, Paul died. He had not made any lifetime transfers. His estate was worth £700,000, to be divided equally between his two sons.

Calculate the Inheritance Tax due on:

- Mary's estate

- Paul's estate

7.3 Christine did not make any lifetime transfers in the previous tax year. During the current tax year she made the following gifts (shown in chronological order):

- £10,000 to her daughter, Rosy, when she got married

- £5,000 to her son, Robert, when he got divorced

- £1,000 to charity

- £500 to the Labour Party

- £2,500 to her parents to pay for them to go on holiday

- £15,000 to her husband, Roger, to buy a new car

Calculate the amount of each potentially exempt transfer made in the current tax year. Show clearly the use of each annual exemption where applicable.

7.4 Jonathan (who had not made any transfers in recent tax years) made the following lifetime transfers:

31 December 2014 £170,000 payment into a trust (a chargeable transfer)

30 April 2015 £20,000 to his son, David

31 May 2015 £30,000 to his daughter, Masie on her birthday

On 30 September 2016, Jonathan died and left an estate valued at £630,000. Jonathan's will listed the following beneficiaries:

- £250,000 to be paid to his wife, Julie

- £5,000 to be given to charity

- The balance to be shared equally between David and Masie

Required:

Calculate:

- The inheritance Tax payable during Jonathan's lifetime

- The inheritance Tax payable on Jonathan's death

7.5 Jim had made no lifetime transfers. When he died he left an estate valued at £800,000 and the following bequests:

- £200,000 to his wife

- £100,000 to charity

- The balance to his daughter

Calculate:

- The Inheritance Tax payable

- The amount that his daughter will receive

Answers to chapter activities

1 Introduction to income tax

1.1   (b) and (e) False; the remaining statements True

1.2   (a) and (d) False; (b), (c) and (e) True

1.3   All the options can provide sources of information about tax law and its interpretation.

1.4

Sample Income		Income Category
UK dividends	⟶	Savings and Investment Income
Partnership profits	⟶	Trading Income
Rents from land	⟶	Property Income
Earnings from a job	⟶	Employment, Pension and Social Security Income

1.5   (a) and (c) Accruals basis; (b) and (d) Receipts basis

1.6   (b), (c), (e) and (f) Exempt; (a) and (d) Not exempt

1.7   (a), (c), (d) and (f) True; (b) and (e) False

2 Income from property

2.1

	Two bedroom house	One bedroom flat
	£	£
Income	8,500	6,600
Expenses:		
Irrecoverable rent	850	
Management fees	765	
Redecoration	530	
Council Tax & Water		1,100
Insurance		340
Profit	6,355	5,160

2.2

	£	£
Income		12,000
Expenditure:		
Council tax	700	
Water rates	300	
Insurance	380	
Managing agent's charges	1,200	
Replacement furniture	2,100	
		4,680
Assessable Income		7,320

2.3 (a), (c), (d) and (f) Allowable; (b) and (e) Not allowable

2.4 (a), (b), (c), (d) and (f) Allowable; (e) Not allowable

3 Income from savings and investments

3.1 (a), (c), (d) and (e) True; (b) and (f) False

3.2

General Income	£12,000.00	
Less personal allowance	£11,000.00	
Taxable	£1,000.00	
Income tax £1,000.00 x 20%		£200.00
Savings Income	£1,500.00	
Covered by starting rate:		
Income tax £1,500.00 x 0%		£0.00
Dividend Income	£2,000.00	
Covered by dividend allowance		
Income tax £2,000.00 x 0%		£0.00
Total Income Tax		£200.00

3.3

General Income	£15,000.00		
Less personal allowance	£11,000.00		
Taxable	£4,000.00		
Basic rate	£4,000.00 x 20%		£800.00
Savings Income	£2,500.00		
Starting rate:	£1,000.00 x 0%	£0.00	
Personal savings allowance:	£1,000.00 x 0%	£0.00	
Basic rate	£500.00 x 20%	£100.00	
	£2,500.00		£100.00
Dividend Income	£6,000.00		
Dividend allowance	£5,000.00 x 0%	£0.00	
Dividend ordinary rate:	£1,000.00 x 7.5%	£75.00	
	£6,000.00		£75.00
Total Income Tax			£975.00

3.4 **General Income** £10,000.00

Less personal allowance (part) £10,000.00

Taxable £0.00

Savings Income £7,500.00

Less personal allowance (balance) £1,000.00

£6,500.00

Starting rate: £5,000.00 x 0% £0.00

Personal savings allowance: £1,000.00 x 0% £0.00

Basic rate £500.00 x 20% £100.00

£6,500.00 £100.00

Dividend Income £5,000.00

Dividend allowance £5,000.00 x 0% £0.00

Total Income Tax £100.00

3.5 (b), (c), (d) and (f) True; (a) and (e) False

4 Income from employment

4.1

Indicators of Employment	Indicators of Self Employment
Need to do the work yourself	Can employ helper or substitute
Told how, where and when to do work	Decide yourself how, when and where to do work
Work set hours and paid regular wage with sick pay and holidays	Choose work hours and invoice for work done
No risk of capital or losses	Risk own capital and bear losses from work that is not to standard
Employer provides equipment	Provide own equipment
Usually work for one employer	Work for several people or organisations

4.2 **(a)** **(1)** 44 g/km 7%

              (2) 134 g/km 23%

              (3) 151 g/km 27%

              (4) 249 g/km 37%

   (b) **(1)** The cost of the car used in the benefit in kind computation is **£17,000**

              (2) The percentage used in the benefit in kind computation is **33%**

              (3) The assessable benefit for Silvia relating to the car for 2016/17 is **£2,805**

4.3 **(a)** (c) £75,000

   (b) (a) and (c) Yes; (b) No

   (c) (c) £9,600   *Workings: (£9,300 + (3% x £90,000) – £2,400)*

4.4 £75 *Workings: (£16,000 + £14,000)/2 x 4/12 x (3.0% – 1.5%)*

4.5 **(a)** (b) She will have a taxable amount of £875

              Workings: ((10,000 x (50p – 45p)) + (1,500 x (50p – 25p))

   (b) (b) His taxable salary will be reduced by £1,420

              Workings: ((£28,400 x 5%, the employer's contribution is tax-free)

   (c) (b) An allowable deduction of £120. (The net cost to Steve)

   (d) (a) The employer pays a percentage of her salary into the scheme, but Genna does not

5 Preparing income tax computations

5.1

	£
Employment income	47,500
Rental income	10,350
Savings income	700
Dividend income	6,500
Less Personal Allowance	11,000
Taxable income	54,050
Tax Calculation:	
General income (£47,500 + £10,350 − £11,000) £46,850:	
(£32,000 + £4,000 + £2,000 = £38,000) x 20%	7,600.00
(£46,850 − £38,000) x 40%	3,540.00
Savings income £700:	
Personal savings allowance £500 x 0%	0.00
(£700 − £500 = £200) x 40%	80.00
Dividend income £6,500	
Dividend allowance £5,000 x 0%	0.00
(£6,500 − £5,000 = £1,500) x 32.5%	487.50
Tax liability	11,707.50

5.2

Situation	Dave's tax on savings income	Sue's tax on savings income
	£	£
Current position	200	600
All savings in Dave's name	600	0
All savings in Sue's name	0	1,400

5.3

	Normal situation	Replacing carpet and curtains
	£	£
Taxable Income	37,000	31,000
Tax at 20%	6,400	6,200
Tax at 40%	2,000	0
Total Income Tax	8,400	6,200
Net Cost of Replacements		3,800

5.4

Workings:	
	£
Salary	45,000
Car benefit £22,000 x (16% + 12% + 3%)	6,820
Fuel benefit £22,200 x 31%	6,882
Sub total	58,702
Personal allowance	11,000
Taxable income	47,702
Tax at 20%: Band £32,000 + (1,600 x 100/80) = 34,000 x 20%	6,800
Tax at 40%: (£47,702 – £34,000) x 40%	5,481
Total tax liability	12,281

5.5

	£
Employment Income	91,500
Dividends	17,500
	109,000
Personal allowance	7,250
Taxable income	101,750
General income:	
(32,000 + 1,500) x 20%	6,700
(84,250* − 33,500) x 40%	20,300
Dividend income:	
5,000 x 0%	0
12,500 x 32.5%	4,062
Tax liability	31,062

Workings:

Adjusted net income: £91,500 + £17,500 − £1,500 = £107,500

Personal allowance: £11,000 − 50% x (£107,500 − £100,000) = £7,250

*General income: £91,500 − £7,250 = £84,250

6 Capital gains tax

6.1

	Actual proceeds used	Deemed proceeds used	No gain or loss basis
(a) Father gives an asset to his son		✔	
(b) Wife sells an asset to her husband			✔
(c) Simon gives an asset to his friend		✔	
(d) Margaret sells an asset to her cousin for £15,000 when the market value is £40,000	✔		
(e) Brian gives an asset to his civil partner, Dave			✔

6.2   (c)   £4,190

True: legal fees are an allowable deduction where they relate to the purchase or sale of an asset.

6.3   (a), (b), (c) and (e) True; (d) False

6.4   **(a)**   The gain on the asset is **£12,500**

(b)   The amount of loss that will be relieved is **£1,400**

(c)   The capital gains tax payable is **£0**

(d)   The loss to be carried forward to the next tax year is **£2,600**

6.5

Asset	Exempt	Chargeable
Antique furniture valued at £30,000		✔
Principal private residence	✔	
Clock	✔	
Shares		✔
Holiday home		✔
Government securities	✔	
Vintage car	✔	
Land		✔

6.6 **(a)**

Occupation / Deemed Occupation	Non-occupation
1/1/2000 - 31/12/2002 (36 months)	
1/1/2003 - 31/12/2003 (12 months)	
1/1/2004 - 30/6/2005 (18 months)	
1/7/2005 - 31/12/2012 (90 months)	1/1/2013 - 30/6/2015 (30 months)
1/7/2015 - 1/1/2017 (18 months)	

(b) Chargeable gain is **£11,765** *Workings: ((£205,000 – £125,000) x 30/204)*

6.7

Asset	Sale proceeds	Cost	Statement
1	£4,000	£7,000	Sale proceeds to be £6,000
2	£14,000	£8,000	Calculate gain as normal
3	£8,000	£3,000	Chattel marginal relief applies
4	£3,000	£5,000	Exempt asset
5	£15,000	£21,000	Calculate loss as normal

6.8

	Number of shares	£
October 2000	20,000	100,000
Bonus	800	0
Sub total	20,800	100,000
Disposal	8,000	38,462
Pool balance	12,800	61,538
Proceeds		72,000
Cost		38,462
Gain		33,538

7 Inheritance tax

7.1

	£
Inheritance Tax calculation:	
Estate	750,000
Less exempt transfer to Phil	(250,000)
Less exempt transfer to charity	(5,000)
Less nil rate band	(325,000)
Amount subject to IHT	170,000
Inheritance tax at 40%	68,000

	£
Calculation of amount received by Robert:	
Estate	750,000
Less transfer to Phil	(250,000)
Less transfer to charity	(5,000)
Less Inheritance Tax	(68,000)
Balance due to Robert	427,000

7.2

	£
Mary's estate:	
Estate	350,000
Less exempt transfer to Paul (£350,000 – £80,000)	(270,000)
Less nil rate band used	(80,000)
Amount subject to IHT	0
Inheritance tax at 40%	0

	£
Paul's estate:	
Estate	700,000
Less nil rate band (£325,000 + (£325,000 – £80,000))	(570,000)
Chargeable to IHT	130,000
Inheritance Tax at 40%	52,000

7.3

	£	£
Gift to daughter, Rosy	10,000	
Less marriage gift exemption	(5,000)	
		5,000
Less current year annual exemption		(3,000)
Less part of prior year annual exemption		(2,000)
The gift to Rosy does not result in PET		0
Gift to son, Robert		5,000
Less balance of prior year annual exemption		(1,000)
PET resulting from gift to Robert		4,000
PET resulting from gift to parents (no deductions)		2,500

The gifts to charity, the Labour Party, and her husband are all exempt transfers.

7.4 Inheritance Tax due in lifetime:

The chargeable transfer will not result in any IHT payable immediately, since (after deducting two £3,000 annual exemptions) it is £164,000, which is below the £325,000 threshold.

The gift to David is a PET of £20,000, less annual exemption of £3,000 = £17,000. The gift to Masie is a PET of £30,000.

Inheritance tax on death:

	£
Estate	630,000
Less exempt transfer to wife, Julie	(250,000)
Less exempt transfer to charity	(5,000)
Less nil rate band	
(£325,000 – £164,000 – £17,000 – £30,000)	(114,000)
Chargeable to IHT	261,000
Inheritance Tax at 40%	104,400

7.5

Inheritance Tax calculation:

	£
Estate	800,000
Less exempt transfer to Jim's wife	(200,000)
Less exempt transfer to charity	(100,000)
Less nil rate band	(325,000)
Amount subject to IHT	175,000
Inheritance tax at 36%*	63,000

*The 'net value' of the estate is (£800,000 – £200,000 – £325,000) = £275,000. The payment to charity of £100,000 is equal to more than 10% of £275,000, and so the rate of 36% applies.

Calculation of amount received by Jim's daughter:

	£
Estate	800,000
Less exempt transfer to Jim's wife	(200,000)
Less exempt transfer to charity	(100,000)
Less Inheritance Tax	(63,000)
Balance due to Jim's daughter	437,000

Practice assessment 1

Task 1

You work for a small firm of accountants. One of your clients has arrived for a meeting to review the accounts and tax work that you have completed for his small business. The business's taxable profits are typically about £60,000 per year, and this year's figures show a similar profit.

The client looks at the figures, and then states 'I don't want to provide HMRC with such a high profit figure. I would like to show profits at nearer £40,000 so that I can avoid the higher rate of tax. I don't mind how you adjust the figures – after all it's just a bit of harmless tax avoidance that everyone does.'

Explain how you will deal with this situation.

Task 2

(a) Joe had two company cars during 2016/17 and his employer paid the running costs of each car, including all fuel. The following table shows the details.

Car	Number of months	List price £	Price paid £	Joe's capital contribution £	Scale charge %
Ford	4	25,350	25,150	1,000	23
Fiat	8	31,250	22,500	6,500	19

Complete the following table to show Joe's taxable benefit in kind for the cars for 2016/17. Show your answers in whole pounds only.

	£
The benefit in kind for the use of the Ford car	
The benefit in kind for the provision of fuel for the Ford car	
The benefit in kind for the use of the Fiat car	
The benefit in kind for the provision of fuel for the Fiat car	

(b) Complete the following table by inserting the scale charge for 2016/17 for each of the cars shown.

	Engine type	CO_2 emissions	Scale charge %
Car 1	Diesel	245	
Car 2	Petrol – electric hybrid	44	

Task 3

The following table shows a list of benefits relating to employment. Enter the assessable amount (or zero for any that are exempt) for each benefit.

	Assessable amount £
Private use of a small van including private fuel from 1 September 2016 until 31 December 2016	
An interest-free loan of £9,000, repayable over 2 years from the loan date of 1 June 2016	
Use of a company flat with an annual value of £5,000. The flat was bought in 2006 for £130,000, and was valued at £200,000 when first occupied by this employee. The flat is not job related	
Use of a home cinema system bought by the employer for £2,000 for the employee's use from 6 June 2016	
A holiday costing £500 was paid for using a company credit card (with the employer's permission)	
A bicycle costing £300 was provided to use both for travelling to work and for leisure	
Free workplace parking in a public car park that costs the employer £2,860 per year	

Task 4

Complete the following sentence for each taxpayer. Enter answers in whole pounds only.

Mabel received a dividend of £7,400. Her other income, before personal allowances was £28,000.

The tax payable on the dividends is £ [   ]

John received £1,650 interest from his bank and £560 interest from his individual savings account. His other taxable income, after the personal allowance was £63,500.

The tax payable on savings income is £ [   ]

Vikram received building society interest of £4,400. His other income was £161,500.

The tax payable on savings income is £ [   ]

Task 5

Complete the following table to show the taxable rent and the allowable expenses for each property. Enter amounts in whole pounds only.

Property	Details	Taxable rent £	Allowable expenses £
10 Major Road	This property was first let on 1 December in the tax year for £800 per month. The tenant paid 6 months' rent in advance, plus a refundable deposit of £1,000. The landlord paid £600 per month to the mortgage provider, which included £375 interest and £65 property insurance.		
2 Little Lane	This property was let all the tax year for £1,200 per month. The managing agent charged 12% of the rent received. The bathroom fittings were replaced costing £1,500.		
4 Manor Park	This property was occupied by the landlord's son until 30 June in the tax year. The interior was then repainted costing £800 and a tenant moved in on 5 July, paying £900 per month. A washing machine was purchased for the property in July costing £550. There had not been one in the property previously.		

Task 6

(a)   Nigel has the following income for the tax year:

Income from employment	£44,500
Property income	£10,350
Bank interest received	£1,380
Dividends received	£6,400

Nigel has property income losses brought forward of £2,100.

During the tax year, Nigel made gifts to charities under gift-aid of £1,840.

Using the blank table below, calculate Nigel's total income tax liability.

(b)   Gemma has employment income of £45,000, plus bank interest of £950. She has read that interest can be tax-free up to £1,000 per year. Explain to Gemma the rules about how much personal savings allowance individuals are entitled to.

Task 7

During the tax year, Celia received a gross salary of £53,500 and use of a company car with an assessable benefit value of £6,150.

Complete the following table to show the National Insurance Contributions relating to Celia in whole pounds. Ignore the employment allowance.

	£
The total Class 1 NIC payable by Celia in the tax year	
The total Class 1 NIC payable by Celia's employer in the tax year	
The total Class 1A NIC payable by Celia's employer relating to the tax year	

Task 8

(a)   Indicate with ticks whether each of the following statements is true or false.

	True	False
(a) For an interest-free personal loan from an employer to be an exempt benefit the total loan(s) must not exceed £10,000 during the tax year		
(b) A transfer of money to a husband, wife, or civil partner has no implications for either Capital Gains Tax or Inheritance Tax		

(b)   Complete the sentences below.

Dick and Jane are married. They have £60,000 to invest in a savings account that pays 2% interest per year. They have no other savings income. Dick's employment income is £21,000 per year, and Jane's employment income is £63,000 per year.

If the £60,000 is invested in a savings account in Dick's name the tax payable will be

£ [   ]   less than if it is invested in Jane's name.

Julie has total income of £110,000 per year. If she pays £4,000 (net) to a charity under gift aid,

her personal allowance will increase by £ [   ]

Rashid will have use of a diesel company car for the whole tax year with a list price of £30,000, and car benefit of 25%. He is a higher-rate taxpayer. If Rashid changes this car to a petrol model with the same list price, but a CO_2 figure 10 g/km lower it would save him

£ [   ]   per year in tax (excluding fuel benefit).

Task 9

(a)   For each statement, tick the appropriate box.

	Actual proceeds used	Deemed proceeds used	No gain or loss basis
(1) Dave gives an asset to his father			
(2) Peter sells an asset to his friend			
(3) Simon gives an asset to his friend			

(b)   John has a capital loss brought forward of £2,500. He has taxable income for the year of £25,000.

He sold an asset during the tax year for £21,000 (not residential property). He had been left the asset when his grandfather died. His grandfather had paid £6,000 for the asset, and it was valued at £9,500 at the time of death.

Complete the following sentences:

(1)   The gain on the asset is £ [   ]

(2)   The amount of loss that will be relieved is £ [   ]

(3)   The capital gains tax payable is £ [   ]

(4)   The loss to be carried forward to the next tax year is £ [   ]

(c)   Complete the following table to show which assets are exempt from capital gains tax and which are chargeable.

Asset	Exempt	Chargeable
Land		
Principal private residence		
Antique painting valued at £20,000		
Unquoted shares		
Caravan		
Government securities		
Classic car		
Horse		

Task 10

Pam bought 25,000 shares in Lester Ltd for £5 per share in October 2000. In April 2005 she took up a rights issue of 3 for 5 at £4 per share. In January 2017, Pam sold 10,000 shares for £8 per share.

Clearly showing the balance of shares, and their value to carry forward, calculate the gain made on these shares. All workings must be shown in your calculations.

Task 11

The following information is available about four taxpayers who sold capital assets (not residential property) during the tax year. These were their only capital asset disposals. Complete the table to show the capital gains tax payable by each individual, in whole pounds.

Taxpayer	Sold to	Proceeds £	Market value £	Cost £	Other taxable income £	Capital Gains Tax £
Dave	Son	31,500	40,000	25,000	48,000	
Brian	Wife	10,000	50,000	45,000	63,000	
Sue	Friend	15,000	18,000	14,000	21,000	
Alison	Friend	33,000	25,000	13,500	30,000	

Task 12

(a) The following lifetime transfers were made by unconnected individuals. Complete the table to show the value of any potentially exempt transfers, assuming that the annual exempt amounts for the current and previous year have already been utilised. If any transfers are wholly exempt enter a zero.

	Value of PET £
Gill gives Dave £5,000 to celebrate their forthcoming marriage	
Roger donates £10,000 to the National Trust (a registered charity)	
Sue gives her daughter £10,000 to help with a house deposit	

(b) Analyse the following statements about Inheritance Tax into those that are true and those that are false.

	True	False
(a) Individuals that are not domiciled in the UK are always liable for IHT on transfers of their worldwide property		
(b) Individuals that are resident and domiciled in the UK are liable for IHT on transfers of their worldwide property		
(c) A donation to a qualifying political party is an exempt transfer whether made during the individual's lifetime or on death		

Task 13

June and Brian were married. Brian died in 2014, leaving an estate valued at £200,000, having made no lifetime gifts. Brian's estate was not left to June.

June died in 2017, leaving an estate valued at £950,000. Her will stated that £15,000 was to be left to a charity, and the balance of her estate to her only child. June had made no lifetime gifts.

Using the blank table below, calculate the Inheritance Tax payable on June's estate, showing your workings.

Practice assessment 2

Task 1

You work for a small firm of accountants. One of your clients is self employed in the entertainment industry, and an additional rate taxpayer. She has arrived for a meeting that she requested.

She explains that she has been introduced to a 'tax minimisation specialist' who has recommended that she joins a tax avoidance scheme. The scheme involves using various offshore companies which can divert her earnings through a complicated system. She understands that this will save her 'a substantial amount of tax'. She has also been told that HMRC is 'aware of the scheme'.

The client is keen to go ahead, and asks you to explain the differences between tax avoidance and tax evasion, and any implications of joining the scheme.

Give your response in the box below, and note briefly the ethical implications.

Task 2

(a)   Miranda had the use of two company cars during the tax year. The company paid for all the running costs of the cars, including all fuel.

Details of the cars are as follows:

Car	Period of use	List price £	Cost £	CO_2 emissions	Type of engine
Ford	5 months of the tax year	28,500	27,600	139 g/km	Petrol
Citroen	7 months of the tax year	29,060	29,000	85 g/km	Diesel Hybrid

Complete the following table to show Miranda's taxable benefit in kind for the cars for the tax year. Show amounts in whole pounds.

Car		%	£
Ford	Scale charge percentage		
	Taxable benefit on provision of the car		
	Taxable benefit on provision of fuel		
Citroen	Scale charge percentage		
	Taxable benefit on provision of the car		
	Taxable benefit on provision of fuel		
Total taxable benefit			

(b)   Complete the following table by inserting the scale charge for 2016/17 for each of the cars shown.

	Engine type	CO_2 emissions	Scale charge %
Car 1	Petrol	185	
Car 2	Electric	0	

Task 3

(a) Indicate whether each of the following will or will not result in an assessable benefit in kind for the employee by ticking the appropriate box.

The following are provided by the employer to the employee	Assessable benefit in kind	Not assessable benefit in kind
(a) Use of a bicycle and helmet to commute to work		
(b) Subscription to gym that is also used by non-employees		
(c) Allowance of £5 per night for incidental costs while staying away from home on business		
(d) Relocation costs of £5,000 when required to move house by the employer		

(b) Robert was provided with the following by his employer during the tax year:

- A new computer games console to use at home for the whole tax year. This cost the employer £350, and remains the employer's property. By the end of the tax year the console was valued at £100.

- An interest free loan of £14,000 at the start of the tax year. Robert repaid £6,000 on 6 January 2017, but made no other repayments.

- Mileage allowance of 60p per mile for business journeys using Robert's own car. Robert claimed for trips totalling 13,000 miles.

Complete the following table to show the total assessable benefits (if any).

	Assessable amount £
Use of computer games console	
Interest free loan	
Mileage allowance	

Task 4

Complete the following sentence for each taxpayer. Enter answers in whole pounds only.

Mary received a dividend of £6,200. Her other income, after the personal allowance was £21,500.

The tax payable on the dividends is £ [   ]

Joe received £650 interest from his bank and £1,560 interest from his individual savings account. His other taxable income, after the personal allowance was £46,500.

The tax payable on savings income is £ [   ]

Alex received dividend income of £4,150. His other income was £152,500.

The tax payable on dividend income is £ [   ]

Task 5

Complete the following table to show the taxable rent and the allowable expenses for each property. Enter amounts in whole pounds only.

Property	Details	Taxable rent £	Allowable expenses £
12 Water Road	This property was let for the whole tax year for £900 per month. The landlord paid £400 per month mortgage interest and £85 per month property insurance. The property flooded in December. The insurance company paid £4,000 out of the £4,500 cost of repairs.		
Upper Lodge	This property was let until 30 June for £1,200 per month. The property was then empty until 1 August, when it was let for the rest of the tax year at £1,250 per month. The managing agent charged 12% of the rent received. The carpets were replaced costing £1,200 during July.		
Manor House	This property was let out until 31 January in the tax year at £1,800 per month. The tenant moved out, owing rent for December and January, and cannot be located. The interior was then repainted costing £1,700 and a new tenant moved in on 5 April. Insurance costs were £60 per month throughout the tax year.		

Task 6

(a) Sadiq has the following income for the tax year:

Income from employment	£47,100
Property income	£6,060
Bank interest received	£780
Dividends received	£5,200

Sadiq has property income losses brought forward of £8,100.

During the tax year, Sadiq made net payments into a personal pension scheme of £2,000.

Using the blank table below, calculate Sadiq's total income tax liability.

(b)   Nada has employment income of £15,000, plus bank interest of £2,500. Explain to Nada how the tax on her savings income will be calculated.

Task 7

During the tax year, Donna received a gross salary of £43,900 and benefits in kind with an assessable value of £10,400.

Complete the following table to show the National Insurance Contributions relating to Donna in whole pounds. Ignore the employment allowance.

	£
The total Class 1 NIC payable by Donna in the tax year	
The total Class 1 NIC payable by Donna's employer in the tax year	
The total Class 1A NIC payable by Donna's employer relating to the tax year	

Task 8

(a) Indicate with ticks whether each of the following statements is true or false.

	True	False
(a) For a personal loan from an employer to be an assessable benefit the total loan(s) must exceed £10,000 during the tax year and the interest rate must be lower than the official rate		
(b) When an individual transfers their cash ISA to a different provider they lose the tax free status of the interest for the current tax year		

(b) Complete the sentences below.

Paul and Cath are married. They are considering buying 20,000 shares in a company that consistently pays dividends of 40 pence per share each year. Paul's employment income is £32,000 per year, and Cath's employment income is £58,000 per year. They have no other income.

If the shares are bought in Paul's name the tax payable on the dividends will be

£ [   ] less than if they are bought in Cath's name.

Joan has total income of £110,000 per year, including provisional property income of £20,000.

If Joan spends an extra £3,000 replacing a carpet in a rental property she will save tax of

£ [   ]

Roger will have use of a diesel company car for the whole tax year, together with free fuel. The car benefit is 30%. He is a higher-rate taxpayer. If Roger changes this car to a petrol model with a CO_2 figure 35 g/km lower it would save him annual tax on just the fuel benefit of

£ [   ]

Task 9

(a)   Indicate whether each of the following statements is true or false.

		True	False
(a)	A chattel bought and sold for less than £6,000 is exempt from capital gains tax		
(b)	Transfers between spouses are carried out on a 'no gain, no loss' basis		
(c)	Capital gains tax will be incurred on the increase in value of investments between the date of purchase and the date of the owners' death		
(d)	Mechanical chattels (for example clocks) owned for personal use are exempt from capital gains tax		

(b)   Josie bought a painting for £14,000 and spent £3,000 having it restored and £800 insuring it. She sold it for £16,000.

Select the capital gain or loss on disposal from the following:

(a)	Zero (exempt asset)	
(b)	Gain of £2,000	
(c)	Loss of £1,000	
(d)	Loss of £1,800	

(c)   Jack's grandfather, John, bought an asset for £6,600. Some years later John died and left the asset to Jack in his will. The asset was valued at £9,400 at that time.

Recently, Jack sold the asset to his sister, Jill, for £6,000 when it was valued at £11,000.

Complete the following table to calculate the gain or loss when Jack sold the asset to Jill. Use a minus sign to denote a loss.

	£
Proceeds or deemed proceeds	
Cost or deemed cost	
Gain or loss	

Task 10

Ken bought 800 shares in Kandle Ltd for £3,000 in April 2003. In May 2009 he bought a further 1,200 shares for £3.90 each. In December 2010 a rights issue of 1 for 5 at £2.00 per share was offered, and Ken took up the offer.

Ken sold 500 shares on 11 November 2016 for a total of £3,000. On 23 December 2016 he purchased a further 100 shares for £6.30 each.

Clearly showing the balance of shares and their value to carry forward, calculate the gain made on the sale of shares that occurred in 2016/17.

Task 11

The following information is available about four taxpayers who sold capital assets (not residential property) during the tax year. These were their only capital asset disposals. Complete the table to show the capital gains tax payable by each individual, in whole pounds.

Taxpayer	Sold to	Proceeds	Market value	Cost	Other taxable income	Capital Gains Tax
		£	£	£	£	£
Adam	Cousin	41,500	50,000	29,000	58,000	
Ben	Wife	35,000	40,000	20,000	23,000	
Chloe	Stranger	25,000	28,000	12,000	21,000	
Della	Friend	23,000	35,000	10,500	31,000	

Task 12

(a) The following lifetime transfers were the only gifts made in the tax year by unconnected individuals. Complete the table to show the value of any potentially exempt transfers, assuming that the annual exempt amounts for the current and previous year have not been utilised. If any transfers are wholly exempt enter a zero.

	Value of PET £
Sue gives her daughter £12,000 to celebrate her marriage	
Roger donates £20,000 to a qualifying political party	
Richard gives his son £25,000 to help with a house deposit	

(b) Analyse the following statements about Inheritance Tax into those that are true and those that are false.

	True	False
(a) The annual allowance of £3,000 can be used as a deduction from a death estate		
(b) Taper relief can reduce the tax rate at death where lifetime transfers were made between three and seven years before death		
(c) When any amount is bequeathed to charity at death, the tax rate on the chargeable part of the estate is reduced to 36%		

Task 13

The only lifetime transfer made by Helen was a PET of £400,000 (after exemptions) made on 31 December 2010.

Helen died on 31 January 2017, leaving an estate valued at £50,000 to her son.

Using the blank table below, calculate the Inheritance Tax payable due to Helen's death, showing your workings.

Practice
assessment 3

Task 1

You work for a small firm of accountants. One of your clients for accounts and tax work owns a business that acts as a wholesaler of DIY products. You are concerned about several large receipts and payments through the business bank account that do not appear to have any documentation.

The client has been asked what the transactions relate to. He has explained that all the transactions relate to his brother-in-law's restaurant business. 'He needed to reduce his cash balance for some reason. I said that he could put some money in my account and that I would invoice him later on for something. When he wanted the money back we could call it 'management charges' or something. We haven't got around to doing the paperwork yet. Maybe you can help with this.'

Explain in the box below how the situation should be dealt with.

Task 2

(a)   Dirk is a senior manager in the defence industry. During the tax year he was provided with the following company cars:

From the start of the tax year until 30 June he was provided with a Jaguar. It was purchased for £41,000 second hand, and had a list price of £52,000. Its emissions were 152 g/km and it was powered by a petrol engine.

Following a promotion for Dirk, the Jaguar was replaced with a new diesel powered Range Rover on 1 July. This car had a list price of £72,000. The company believed that Dirk's new role placed him at increased risk of a terrorism attack, and paid £25,000 for the Range Rover to be equipped with bullet resistant glass and strengthened bodywork. The emissions of the car were 230 g/km. On 1 December the car was fitted with passengers' televisions so that Dirk's family could be entertained on long trips. This cost the company £1,200.

Complete the following table to show the 2016/17 benefit in kind arising from the use of these cars. Ignore any benefit arising from private fuel.

Car	Percentage applicable based on CO₂ emissions %	Cost of car used in benefit calculation £	Benefit in kind £
Jaguar			
Range Rover			
Total			

(b)   Complete the following table by inserting the scale charge for 2016/17 for each of the cars shown.

	Engine type	CO₂ emissions	Scale charge %
Car 1	Diesel	142	
Car 2	Petrol	158	

Task 3

(a) Place a tick in the appropriate column of the table below to show whether each of the items listed would or would not result in an assessable benefit in kind for an employee.

The following are provided by the employer to the employee	Benefit in kind	No benefit in kind
(a) Use of a company credit card to pay for the entertainment ofcustomers (with approval of the employer)		
(b) Mileage payment for use of employee's own motorcycle for business purposes at a rate of 24p per mile		
(c) Petrol for travel from home to work in a company car		
(d) Training costs including course and examination fees for accountancy trainee undertaking AAT course		

(b) Calculate the assessable benefit in kind (in whole pounds) for each of the following:

	Benefit £
On 6 April an employee was provided with an interest free loan of £15,000. During the tax year he made three repayments, each of £2,000. The remainder of the loan was still outstanding at the end of the tax year.	
On 6 April an employee was allowed the use of a home cinema system that had previously been used by the company. The home cinema had originally cost the company £1,500, but its market value on 6 April was £1,000.	

(c)   Using the following table, analyse the benefits into those that are exempt from tax, and those that are taxable.

Description	Exempt	Taxable
Provision of a chauffeur for business and private journeys		
Long service award in cash for employee with 10 years' service		
Counselling services		
Free meals in a staff restaurant available to all staff		
Provision of free UK health insurance		

(d)   Tick the appropriate box to show whether each of the following situations would increase or reduce an employee's tax liability under the approved mileage allowance payments scheme.

Business mileage and rate paid	Increase tax liability	Reduce tax liability
5,000 miles at 50p per mile		
15,000 miles at 45p per mile		
15,000 miles at 38p per mile		
20,000 miles at 25p per mile		

Task 4

Complete the following sentence for each taxpayer. Enter answers in whole pounds only.

Monica received a dividend of £6,000. Her other income was £151,500.

The tax payable on the dividends is £ [   ]

Jonathan received £2,650 interest from his bank. His only other income was employment income of £14,000.

The tax payable on savings income is £ [   ]

Alan received dividend income of £6,200. His other income, before the personal allowance, was £52,500.

The tax payable on dividend income is £ [   ]

Task 5

Complete the following table to show the taxable rent and the allowable expenses for each property. Enter amounts in whole pounds only.

Property	Details	Taxable rent £	Allowable expenses £
1 Henry Road	This property was let for the whole tax year for £950 per month. The landlord paid £500 per month mortgage interest and £40 per month property insurance. During the year, the landlord installed central heating where none existed previously, costing £6,000.		
Middle House	This property was let until 30 September for £1,000 per month. The property was then used as a second home by the landlord. The mortgage interest was £450 per month, and buildings insurance was £240 per year.		
3 Lincoln Road	This property was let out until 31 January in the tax year at £800 per month. The interior was then decorated costing £1,200 and the carpets were replaced costing £1,800. A new tenant moved in on 1 March paying £820 per month.		

Task 6

(a)   Sarah has the following income for the tax year:

Income from employment	£37,100
Property income	£8,150
Bank interest received	£1,780
Dividends received	£4,200

During the tax year, Sarah made net payments into a personal pension scheme of £800.

Using the blank table below, calculate Sarah's total income tax liability.

(b) Nadia has employment income of £41,000, plus dividend income of £7,500. Explain to Nadia how the tax on her dividend income will be calculated.

Task 7

During the tax year, Ellen received a gross salary of £8,100 and benefits in kind with an assessable value of £400.

Complete the following table to show the National Insurance Contributions relating to Ellen in whole pounds. Ignore the employment allowance.

	£
The total Class 1 NIC payable by Ellen in the tax year	
The total Class 1 NIC payable by Ellen's employer in the tax year	
The total Class 1A NIC payable by Ellen's employer relating to the tax year	

Task 8

(a)   Indicate with ticks whether each of the following statements is true or false.

		True	False
(a)	If a wholly electric car is provided as a company car the benefit percentage will be 7% for use of the car and any electricity charging provided by the employer will be tax free		
(b)	Individuals aged 18 or over can move their investment from a cash ISA to a stocks and shares ISA without any restrictions		

(b)   Complete the sentences below.

Peter is a basic rate taxpayer in the current year, but will be a higher rate taxpayer next year. He currently has no savings income, but has recently been given £50,000 from his late uncle's estate. He is considering a one year savings account that has two options for receiving interest. A monthly interest option would give him interest of £400 this tax year and £600 next tax year. An annual interest option would mean that he receives £1,000 next tax year.

If the monthly interest option is chosen, then over the two tax years Peter will pay

£ [   ] less tax on savings income than if the annual interest option is chosen.

Jo has total income of £106,000 per year. If Jo earned a further £1,000 as an employment bonus her tax would increase by £ [   ]

Roland is a basic rate taxpayer. His employer has offered a scheme in which Roland's pay would reduce by £55 per week, but he would be given childcare vouchers to the same value.

In a full tax year, this would save Roland Income Tax of £ [   ]

Task 9

(a)   A taxpayer had previously bought an asset for £14,000, plus 6% auction commission. He sold it during the tax year for £15,000, having spent £100 to advertise it for sale. The cost of insuring the asset during his ownership was £150.

Calculate the gain or loss using the following computation.

	Amount £
Proceeds	
Total costs	
Gain / Loss	

(b)   Complete the following table to show which statements are true and which are false in connection with capital gains tax.

Statement	True	False
(a) Gifts to charities are exempt from capital gains tax		
(b) Gifts between a father and son are exempt from capital gains tax		
(c) When applying the 5/3 restriction to chattels, the proceeds figure used is before any costs of sale are deducted		
(d) Chattels are defined as tangible moveable property		
(e) Non-wasting chattels are exempt from capital gains tax		

(c)   Complete the following sentences.

A taxpayer had capital losses brought forward of £6,000. During the tax year he made two disposals, making a gain of £16,300 on one and a loss of £1,900 on the other.

The amount subject to capital gains tax for the year (after the annual exempt amount) will be:

£ [   ]

The capital loss to be carried forward to be set against future gains will be:

£ [   ]

Task 10

Paul bought 18,000 shares in Leicester Ltd for £4.50 per share in October 2000. In April 2012 he took up a rights issue of 4 for 9 at £3 per share. In January 2017, Paul sold 12,000 shares for £6 per share.

Clearly showing the balance of shares, and their value to carry forward, calculate the gain made on these shares. All workings must be shown in your calculations.

Task 11

The following information is available about four taxpayers who sold capital assets (not residential property) during the tax year. These were their only capital asset disposals. Complete the table to show the capital gains tax payable by each individual, in whole pounds.

Taxpayer	Sold to	Proceeds £	Market value £	Cost £	Other taxable income £	Capital Gains Tax £
Ella	Grandfather	48,500	55,000	24,000	58,000	
Fred	Civil Partner	29,000	40,000	12,000	20,000	
Gareth	Stranger	25,000	20,000	10,000	22,000	
Helen	Friend	20,000	32,000	8,500	45,000	

Task 12

(a) The following lifetime transfers were the only gifts made in the tax year by unconnected individuals. Complete the table to show the value of any potentially exempt transfers, assuming that the annual exempt amounts for the current and previous year have not been utilised. If any transfers are wholly exempt enter a zero.

	Value of PET £
Stan gives his son £15,000 to celebrate his marriage	
Ron donates £2,000 to a museum	
Robert gives his nephew £15,000 to help with a house deposit	

(b) Analyse the following statements about Inheritance Tax into those that are true and those that are false.

	True	False
(a) The annual allowance of £3,000 can only be carried forward for one tax year		
(b) Taper relief can reduce the tax rate at death where lifetime transfers were made between zero and three years before death		
(c) When more than 10% of the net value of an estate is bequeathed to charity at death, the tax rate on the chargeable part of the estate is reduced to 36%		

Task 13

The only lifetime transfer made by Ivor was a chargeable transfer to a trust of £100,000 (after exemptions) made on 31 December 2012.

Ivor died on 31 January 2017, leaving an estate valued at £450,000 to his son.

Using the blank table below, calculate any Inheritance Tax payable during Ivor's lifetime and on Ivor's death, showing your workings.

Answers to practice assessment 1

Task 1

The accounts and tax work that has already been undertaken should be reviewed with the client to ensure that all allowances have been accounted for in the most tax-efficient manner. This is normal tax minimisation.

What the client is proposing is illegal tax evasion, not legal tax avoidance. The suggestion is that the accounts are manipulated to reduce the amount of tax that appears to be due. Tax evasion is a criminal activity.

The AAT Code of Professional Ethics makes it clear that accountancy and tax work must be carried out with professional competence and be consistent with the law. To 'adjust' the figures in the way suggested would not be consistent with the law, and must not be carried out.

Although the client would bear ultimate responsibility for submissions made to HMRC, we cannot be associated with any submission that we believe contains inaccuracies.

The client should be asked to reconsider his request that we alter the figures, and asked to agree to submit the original data. If he refuses then we should cease to act for him.

We would then inform HMRC that we no longer act for the client. The reason for ceasing to act would not normally be given to HMRC, as this would be a breach of confidentiality. There appears to be no suggestion here of money laundering which could override the rules regarding confidentiality.

Task 2

(a)

	£
The benefit in kind for the use of the Ford car	1,867
The benefit in kind for the provision of fuel for the Ford car	1,702
The benefit in kind for the use of the Fiat car	3,325
The benefit in kind for the provision of fuel for the Fiat car	2,812

(b)

	Engine type	CO_2 emissions	Scale charge %
Car 1	Diesel	245	37
Car 2	Petrol – electric hybrid	44	7

Task 3

	Assessable amount
	£
Private use of a small van including private fuel from 1 September 2016 until 31 December 2016	1,256
An interest-free loan of £9,000, repayable over 2 years from the loan date of 1 June 2016	0
Use of a company flat with an annual value of £5,000. The flat was bought in 2006 for £130,000, and was valued at £200,000 when first occupied by this employee. The flat is not job related	8,750
Use of a home cinema system bought by the employer for £2,000 for the employee's use from 6 June 2016	333
A holiday costing £500 was paid for using a company credit card (with the employer's permission)	500
A bicycle costing £300 was provided to use both for travelling to work and for leisure	0
Free workplace parking in a public car park that costs the employer £2,860 per year	0

Task 4

The tax payable on the dividends is £**180**

The tax payable on savings income is £**460**

The tax payable on savings income is £**1,980**

Task 5

Property	Taxable rent £	Allowable expenses £
10 Major Road	3,200	1,760
2 Little Lane	14,400	3,228
4 Manor Park	8,100	800

Task 6

(a)

	Workings	£
Employment income		44,500
Property income	£10,350 – £2,100	8,250
Savings income		1,380
Dividend income		6,400
Less personal allowance		11,000
Taxable income		49,530
General income £41,750	£44,500 + £8,250 – £11,000	
Tax on general income:	(£32,000 + (£1,840/0.8)) x 20%	6,860
	£7,450 x 40%	2,980
Tax on savings income:	£500 x 0%	0
	£880 x 40%	352
Tax on dividend income:	£5,000 x 0%	0
	£1,400 x 32.5%	455
Tax liability		10,647

(b)   Savings income (eg bank interest) is tax-free for basic rate taxpayers up to £1,000 per year. For higher rate taxpayers like Gemma the tax-free amount is up to £500, so the remaining £450 would be taxable (at the higher rate). Additional rate taxpayers are not entitled to any personal savings allowance.

Although the savings income covered by the personal savings allowance is tax free, it still counts within the band, so can push dividend income into the next band.

Task 7

	£
The total Class 1 NIC payable by Celia in the tax year	4,402
The total Class 1 NIC payable by Celia's employer in the tax year	6,263
The total Class 1A NIC payable by Celia's employer relating to the tax year	848

Task 8

(a) Both are True

(b) If the £60,000 is invested in a savings account in Dick's name the tax payable will be **£240** less than if it is invested in Jane's name.

Julie has total income of £110,000 per year. If she pays £4,000 (net) to a charity under gift aid, her personal allowance will increase by **£2,500**.

If Rashid changes this car to a petrol model with the same list price, but a CO_2 figure 10 g/km lower it would save him **£600** per year in tax (excluding fuel benefit).

Task 9

(a)

	Actual proceeds used	Deemed proceeds used	No gain or loss basis
(1) Dave gives an asset to his father		✔	
(2) Peter sells an asset to his friend	✔		
(3) Simon gives an asset to his friend		✔	

(b) **(1)** The gain on the asset is **£11,500**

(2) The amount of loss that will be relieved is **£400**

(3) The capital gains tax payable is **£0**

(4) The loss to be carried forward to the next tax year is **£2,100**

(c)

Asset	Exempt	Chargeable
Land		✔
Principal private residence	✔	
Antique painting valued at £20,000		✔
Unquoted shares		✔
Caravan	✔	
Government securities	✔	
Classic car	✔	
Horse	✔	

Task 10

	Number of Shares	Value £
Purchase	25,000	125,000
Rights	15,000	60,000
Sub total	40,000	185,000
Disposal	10,000	46,250
Balance	30,000	138,750
Proceeds		80,000
Cost		46,250
Gain		33,750

Task 11

Taxpayer	Sold to	Proceeds	Market value	Cost	Other taxable income	Capital Gains Tax
		£	£	£	£	£
Dave	Son	31,500	40,000	25,000	48,000	780
Brian	Wife	10,000	50,000	45,000	63,000	0
Sue	Friend	15,000	18,000	14,000	21,000	0
Alison	Friend	33,000	25,000	13,500	30,000	1,480

Task 12

(a)

	Value of PET
	£
Gill gives Dave £5,000 to celebrate their forthcoming marriage	2,500
Roger donates £10,000 to the National Trust (a registered charity)	0
Sue gives her daughter £10,000 to help with a house deposit	10,000

(b)   (a) False; (b) and (c) True

Task 13

	Workings / Notes	£
June's estate		950,000
Less exempt transfer	Charity (under 10% net estate)	15,000
Less nil rate band		325,000
Less Brian's unused band	£325,000 – £200,000	125,000
Taxable		485,000
Inheritance Tax	£485,000 x 40%	194,000

Answers to practice assessment 2

Task 1

Tax avoidance is the legal use of claims and allowances to reduce the amount of tax payable. Tax evasion involves using illegal methods to reduce tax. There is a grey area between these two activities, and it is not always clear how HMRC or the courts will define a particular activity or scheme.

Where a scheme relies on concealment, pretence, non-disclosure or misrepresentation, this would be categorised as tax evasion which can result in criminal prosecution.

'Aggressive' tax avoidance schemes may also be examined under the recent General Anti-Abuse Rule (GAAR) legislation which will consider whether the law is being used in the way that Parliament originally anticipated.

If HMRC are aware of a particular scheme it does not mean that they have approved it as being legal. There could be ongoing investigations into the scheme which could result in it being declared illegal. Taxpayers must disclose their use of avoidance schemes, and will consequently be viewed as high risk individuals by HMRC. Their tax affairs may be subject to more scrutiny as a result.

Accountants should also consider their own ethical position when clients wish to undertake tax avoidance, and distance themselves from situations that do not meet their own or their professional body's ethical standards. They must also consider any reputational damage that may occur as a result of facilitating their clients' involvement in particular schemes.

Task 2

(a)

Car		%	£
Ford	Scale charge percentage	24	
	Taxable benefit on provision of the car		2,850
	Taxable benefit on provision of fuel		2,220
Citroen	Scale charge percentage	18	
	Taxable benefit on provision of the car		3,051
	Taxable benefit on provision of fuel		2,331
Total taxable benefit			10,452

(b)

	Engine type	CO_2 emissions	Scale charge %
Car 1	Petrol	185	34
Car 2	Electric	0	7

Task 3

(a) **(b)** will result in an assessable benefit in kind; the other options will NOT.

(b)

	Assessable amount £
Use of computer games console	70
Interest free loan	330
Mileage allowance	2,550

Task 4

The tax payable on the dividends is £**90**

The tax payable on savings income is £**60**

The tax payable on dividend income is £**0**

Task 5

Property	Taxable rent £	Allowable expenses £
12 Water Road	10,800	6,320
Upper Lodge	13,600	2,832
Manor House	18,000	6,020

Task 6

(a)

	Workings	£
Employment Income		47,100
Property Income	£6,060 – £8,100 = –£2,040 cf	0
Savings Income		780
Dividend Income		5,200
Less personal allowance		11,000
		42,080
General Income	£47,100 – £11,000 = £36,100	
Basic rate tax	(£32,000 + £2,500) x 20%	6,900
Higher rate tax	(£36,100 – £34,500) x 40%	640
Savings Income	£500 x 0% PSA	0
	£280 x 40%	112
Dividend Income	£5,000 x 0% DA	0
	£200 x 32.5%	65
Tax liability		7,717

(b) Since the taxable general income is £15,000 – £11,000 = £4,000, there is £1,000 left of the £5,000 starting rate band at 0% for savings. The next £1,000 of savings income is covered by the personal savings allowance. This leaves £500 of savings income, and this will be taxed at 20%, equalling £100 tax on savings income.

Task 7

	£
The total Class 1 NIC payable by Donna in the tax year	4,210
The total Class 1 NIC payable by Donna's employer in the tax year	4,938
The total Class 1A NIC payable by Donna's employer relating to the tax year	1,435

Task 8

(a)   (a) True; (b) False

(b)   If the shares are bought in Paul's name the tax payable on the dividends will be **£750** less than if they are bought in Cath's name.

If Joan spends an extra £3,000 replacing a carpet in a rental property she will save tax of **£1,800**.

If Roger changes this car to a petrol model with a CO_2 figure 35 g/km lower it would save him annual tax on just the fuel benefit of **£888**.

Task 9

(a)   (a), (b) and (d) True; (c) False

(b)   (c)   Loss of £1,000

(c)

	£
Proceeds or deemed proceeds	11,000
Cost or deemed cost	9,400
Gain or loss	1,600

Task 10

		Number of shares	Value £
April 2003	Purchase	800	3,000
May 2009	Purchase	1,200	4,680
December 2010	Rights issue	400	800
		2,400	8,480
November 2016	Disposal	500	1,767
	Balance	1,900	6,713
December 2016	Purchase	100	630
	Balance	2,000	7,343
		£	
	Proceeds	3,000	
	Cost	1,767	
	Gain	1,233	

Task 11

Taxpayer	Sold to	Proceeds	Market value	Cost	Other taxable income	Capital Gains Tax
		£	£	£	£	£
Adam	Cousin	41,500	50,000	29,000	58,000	280
Ben	Wife	35,000	40,000	20,000	23,000	0
Chloe	Stranger	25,000	28,000	12,000	21,000	190
Della	Friend	23,000	35,000	10,500	31,000	180

Task 12

(a)

	Value of PET
	£
Sue gives her daughter £12,000 to celebrate her marriage	1,000
Roger donates £20,000 to a qualifying political party	0
Richard gives his son £25,000 to help with a house deposit	19,000

(b)   (b) True; (a) and (c) False

Task 13

	Workings / Notes	£
PET now chargeable	6 to 7 years before death	400,000
Less nil rate band		325,000
Chargeable to IHT		75,000
IHT due on PET (by recipient)	£75,000 x 40% x 20%	6,000
Death estate		50,000
Less nil rate band remaining		0
Chargeable to IHT		50,000
IHT due on estate (by son)	£50,000 x 40%	20,000
Total IHT due	£6,000 + £20,000	£26,000

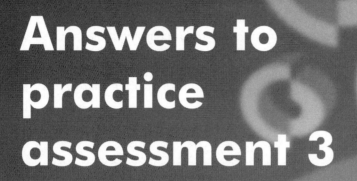

Answers to practice assessment 3

Task 1

It appears that the client is proposing the accounts are falsified to deal with the transactions with his brother-in-law's business. It is also possible that there could be money laundering involved.

The accountancy practice should certainly not become involved with assisting in the creation of fictitious documents or record any transactions in a way that is known to be false.

Advice should be sought from a more senior person within the practice about the best way to proceed. If money laundering is suspected then the normal rules of client confidentiality do not apply and the matter should be reported to the National Crime Agency without alerting the client.

If money laundering is not suspected then the client should be informed that the transactions must be recorded accurately. If the client will not accept this treatment of the transactions, then the practice should cease to act for the client.

Task 2

(a)

Car	Percentage applicable based on CO_2 emissions %	Cost of car used in benefit calculation £	Benefit in kind £
Jaguar	27	52,000	3,510
Range Rover	37	73,200	20,313
Total			23,823

(b)

	Engine type	CO_2 emissions	Scale charge %
Car 1	Diesel	142	28
Car 2	Petrol	158	28

Task 3

(a) (c) will result in an assessable benefit in kind; the other options will NOT.

(b)

	Benefit £
On 6 April an employee was provided with an interest free loan of £15,000. During the tax year he made three repayments, each of £2,000. The remainder of the loan was still outstanding at the end of the tax year.	360
On 6 April an employee was allowed the use of a home cinema system that had previously been used by the company. The home cinema had originally cost the company £1,500, but its market value on 6 April was £1,000.	200

(c)

Description	Exempt	Taxable
Provision of a chauffeur for business and private journeys		✔
Long service award in cash for employee with 10 years' service		✔
Counselling services	✔	
Free meals in a staff restaurant available to all staff	✔	
Provision of free UK health insurance		✔

(d)

Business mileage and rate paid	Increase tax liability	Reduce tax liability
5,000 miles at 50p per mile	✔	
15,000 miles at 45p per mile	✔	
15,000 miles at 38p per mile		✔
20,000 miles at 25p per mile		✔

Task 4

The tax payable on the dividends is £**381**

The tax payable on savings income is £**0**

The tax payable on dividend income is £**390**

Task 5

Property	Taxable rent £	Allowable expenses £
1 Henry Road	11,400	6,480
Middle House	6,000	2,820
3 Lincoln Road	8,820	3,000

Task 6

(a)

	Workings	£
Employment Income		37,100
Property Income		8,150
Savings Income		1,780
Dividend Income		4,200
Less Personal Allowance		11,000
		40,230
General Income £34,250	£37,100 + £8,150 − £11,000	
Basic rate tax	(£32,000 + £1,000) x 20%	6,600
Higher rate	(£34,250 − £33,000) x 40%	500
Savings Income £1,780	£500 x 0% PSA	0
	(£1,780 − £500) x 40%	512
Dividend Income £4,200	£4,200 x 0% DA	0
Tax liability		7,612

(b)   Nadia will be entitled to the dividend allowance that means the first £5,000 of her dividend income will be taxed at 0%. This income still counts within the bands, so this pushes all her remaining dividend of £2,500 into the dividend upper rate band. This is because £41,000 + £5,000 − £11,000 personal allowance = £35,000 which exceeds the £32,000 basic rate band. The remaining £2,500 dividend income will therefore be taxed at 32.5% = £812.50 tax.

Task 7

	£
The total Class 1 NIC payable by Ellen in the tax year	4
The total Class 1 NIC payable by Ellen's employer in the tax year	0
The total Class 1A NIC payable by Ellen's employer relating to the tax year	55

Task 8

(a) Both statements are True

(b) If the monthly interest option is chosen, then over the two tax years Peter will pay £**160** less tax on savings income than if the annual interest option is chosen.

If Jo earned a further £1,000 as an employment bonus her tax would increase by £**600**.

In a full tax year, this would save Roland Income Tax of £**572**.

Task 9

(a)

	Amount £
Proceeds	15,000
Total costs	14,940
Gain	60

(b) (a), (c) and (d) True; (b) and (e) False

(c) The amount subject to capital gains tax for the year (after the annual exempt amount) will be £**0**.

The capital loss to be carried forward to be set against future gains will be £**2,700**.

Task 10

October 2000		18,000	£81,000
April 2012		8,000	£24,000
		26,000	£105,000
Disposal		12,000	£48,462
Pool balance		14,000	£56,538
Proceeds			£72,000
Cost	£48,462		
Gain	£23,538		

Task 11

Taxpayer	Sold to	Proceeds	Market value	Cost	Other taxable income	Capital Gains Tax
		£	£	£	£	£
Ella	Grandfather	48,500	55,000	24,000	58,000	3,980
Fred	Civil Partner	29,000	40,000	12,000	20,000	0
Gareth	Stranger	25,000	20,000	10,000	22,000	390
Helen	Friend	20,000	32,000	8,500	45,000	80

Task 12

(a)

	Value of PET
	£
Stan gives his son £15,000 to celebrate his marriage	4,000
Ron donates £2,000 to a museum	0
Robert gives his nephew £15,000 to help with a house deposit	9,000

(b)   (a) and (c) True; (b) False

Task 13

	Workings / Notes	£
Tax payable during lifetime	No tax as transfer below nil band	0
Tax calculation on death		
Estate		450,000
Less nil rate band	£325,000 – £100,000	225,000
Chargeable to IHT		225,000
Inheritance Tax	£225,000 x 40%	90,000

Reference Material

for AAT Assessment of Personal Tax

Finance Act 2016

Professional conduct in relation to taxation

For assessments from 1 January – 31 December 2017

Note: this reference material is accessible by candidates during their live computer-based assessment for Personal Tax.

This material was current at the time this book was published, but may be subject to change. Readers are advised to check the AAT website or Osborne Books website for any updates.

Reference material for AAT assessment of Personal Tax

Introduction
This document comprises data that you may need to consult during your Personal Tax computer-based assessment. The material can be consulted during the sample and live assessments through pop-up windows. It is made available here so you can familiarise yourself with the content before the test.

Do not take a print of this document into the exam room with you. Unless you need a printed version as part of reasonable adjustments for particular needs, in which case you must discuss this with your tutor at least six weeks before the assessment date.

This document may be changed to reflect periodical updates in the computer-based assessment, so please check you have the most recent version while studying. This version is based on Finance Act 2016 and is for use in AAT assessments 1 January – 31 December 2017.

1. Interpretation and abbreviations

Context

Tax advisers operate in a complex business and financial environment. The increasing public focus on the role of taxation in wider society means a greater interest in the actions of tax advisers and their clients.

This guidance, written by the professional bodies for their members working in tax, sets out the hallmarks of a good tax adviser, and in particular the fundamental principles of behaviour that members are expected to follow.

Interpretation

1.1   In this guidance:
- 'Client' includes, where the context requires, 'former client'.
- 'Member' (and 'members') includes 'firm' or 'practice' and the staff thereof.
- For simplicity, 'she' and 'her' are used throughout but should be taken to include 'he' and 'his'.
- Words in the singular include the plural and words in the plural include the singular.

Abbreviations

1.2   The following abbreviations have been used:

CCAB	Consultative Committee of Accountancy Bodies
DOTAS	Disclosure of Tax Avoidance Schemes
GAAP	Generally Accepted Accounting Principles
GAAR	General Anti-Abuse Rule in Finance Act 2013
HMRC	Her Majesty's Revenue and Customs
MLRO	Money Laundering Reporting Officer
NCA	National Crime Agency (previously the Serious Organised Crime Agency, SOCA)
POTAS	Promoters of Tax Avoidance Schemes
SRN	Scheme Reference Number

2. Fundamental principles

Overview of the fundamental principles

2.1 Ethical behaviour in the tax profession is critical. The work carried out by a member needs to be trusted by society at large as well as by clients and other stakeholders. What a member does reflects not just on themselves but on the profession as a whole.

2.2 A member must comply with the following fundamental principles:

Integrity
To be straightforward and honest in all professional and business relationships.

Objectivity
To not allow bias, conflict of interest or undue influence of others to override professional or business judgements.

Professional competence and due care
To maintain professional knowledge and skill at the level required to ensure that a client or employer receives competent professional service based on current developments in practice, legislation and techniques and act diligently and in accordance with applicable technical and professional standards.

Confidentiality
To respect the confidentiality of information acquired as a result of professional and business relationships and, therefore, not disclose any such information to third parties without proper and specific authority, unless there is a legal or professional right or duty to disclose, nor use the information for the personal advantage of the member or third parties.

Professional behaviour
To comply with relevant laws and regulations and avoid any action that discredits the profession.

Each of these fundamental principles is discussed in more detail in the context of taxation services.

3. Tax returns

Definition of tax return (return)

3.1 For the purposes of this Chapter, the term 'return' includes any document or online submission of data that is prepared on behalf of the client for the purposes of disclosing to any taxing authority details that are to be used in the calculation of tax due by a client or a refund of tax due to the client or for other official purposes and, for example, includes:
- Self-assessment returns for income or corporation tax;
- VAT and Customs returns;
- PAYE returns;
- Inheritance tax returns;
- Returns or claims in respect of any other tax or duties where paid to the UK Government or any authority, such as a devolved government.

3.2 A letter giving details in respect of a return or as an amendment to a return including, for example, any voluntary disclosure of an error should be dealt with as if it was a return.

Taxpayer's responsibility

3.3 The taxpayer has primary responsibility to submit correct and complete returns to the best of her knowledge and belief. The return may include reasonable estimates where necessary. It follows that the final decision as to whether to disclose any issue is that of the client.

Member's responsibility

3.4 A member who prepares a return on behalf of a client is responsible to the client for the accuracy of the return based on the information provided.

3.5 In dealing with HMRC in relation to a client's tax affairs a member must bear in mind her duty of confidentiality to the client and that she is acting as the agent of her client. She has a duty to act in the best interests of her client.

3.6 A member must act in good faith in dealings with HMRC in accordance with the fundamental principle of integrity. In particular the member must take reasonable care and exercise appropriate professional scepticism when making statements or asserting facts on behalf of a client. Where acting as a tax agent, a member is not required to audit the figures in the books and records provided or verify information provided by a client or by a third party. A member should take care not to be associated with the presentation of facts she knows or believes to be incorrect or misleading nor to assert tax positions in a tax return which she considers have no sustainable basis.

3.7 When a member is communicating with HMRC, she should consider whether she needs to make it clear to what extent she is relying on information which has been supplied by the client or a third party.

Materiality

3.8 Whether an amount is to be regarded as material depends upon the facts and circumstances of each case.

3.9 The profits of a trade, profession, vocation or property business must be computed in accordance with GAAP subject to any adjustment required or authorised by law in computing profits for those purposes. This permits a trade, profession, vocation or property business to disregard non-material adjustments in computing its accounting profits. However, it should be noted that for certain small businesses an election may be made to use the cash basis instead.

3.10   The application of GAAP, and therefore materiality, does not extend beyond the accounting profits. Thus the accounting concept of materiality cannot be applied when completing tax returns (direct and indirect), for example when:
- computing adjustments required to accounting figures so as to arrive at taxable profits;
- allocating income, expenses and outgoings across the relevant boxes on a self-assessment tax return;
- collating the aggregate figures from all shareholdings and bank accounts for disclosure on tax returns.

Disclosure

3.11   If a client is unwilling to include in a tax return the minimum information required by law, the member should follow the guidance in Chapter 5 Irregularities. 3.12 - 3.18 give guidance on some of the more common areas of uncertainty over disclosure.

3.12   In general, it is likely to be in a client's own interests to ensure that factors relevant to her tax liability are adequately disclosed to HMRC because:
- her relationship with HMRC is more likely to be on a satisfactory footing if she can demonstrate good faith in her dealings with them; and
- she will reduce the risk of a discovery or further assessment and may reduce exposure to interest and penalties.

3.13   It may be advisable to consider fuller disclosure than is strictly necessary. The factors involved in making this decision include:
- the terms of the applicable law;
- the view taken by the member;
- the extent of any doubt that exists;
- the manner in which disclosure is to be made; and
- the size and gravity of the item in question.

3.14   When advocating fuller disclosure than is strictly necessary a member should ensure that her client is adequately aware of the issues involved and their potential implications. Fuller disclosure should not be made unless the client consents to the level of disclosure.

3.15   Cases will arise where there is doubt as to the correct treatment of an item of income or expenditure, or the computation of a gain or allowance. In such cases a member ought to consider carefully what disclosure, if any, might be necessary. For example, additional disclosure should be considered where:
- a return relies on a valuation;
- there is inherent doubt as to the correct treatment of an item, for example, expenditure on repairs which might be regarded as capital in whole or part, or the VAT liability of a particular transaction; or
- HMRC has published its interpretation or has indicated its practice on a point, but the client proposes to adopt a different view, whether or not supported by Counsel's opinion. The member should refer to the guidance on the Veltema case and 3.19.

3.16   A member who is uncertain whether her client should disclose a particular item or of its treatment should consider taking further advice before reaching a decision. She should use her best endeavours to ensure that the client understands the issues, implications and the proposed course of action. Such a decision may have to be justified at a later date, so the member's files should contain sufficient evidence to support the position taken, including contemporaneous notes of discussions with the client and/or with other advisers, copies of any second opinion obtained and the client's final decision. A failure to take reasonable care may result in HMRC imposing a penalty if an error is identified after an enquiry.

3.17 The 2012 case of Charlton clarified the law on discovery in relation to tax schemes disclosed to HMRC under DOTAS. The Upper Tribunal made clear that where the taxpayer has:
(i) disclosed details of a significant allowable loss claim;
(ii) declared relatively modest income/ gains; and/or
(iii) included the SRN issued by HMRC on the appropriate self-assessment tax return,

an HMRC officer of reasonable knowledge and skill would be expected to infer that the taxpayer had entered into a tax avoidance scheme (and that fuller details of such scheme would be contained in the relevant AAG1 Form). As a result, HMRC would be precluded, in most cases, from raising a discovery assessment in a situation where the client implemented the disclosed scheme and HMRC failed to open an enquiry within the required time.

3.18 It is essential where a member is involved in the preparation of a self-assessment tax return which includes a scheme disclosed under DOTAS that the member takes care to ensure:
- that the tax return provides sufficient details of any transactions entered into (in case the AAG1 Form is incomplete);
- that the SRN is recorded properly in the appropriate box included for this purpose on a self-assessment tax return; and
- the SRN is shown for the self-assessment return for each year in which the scheme is expected to give the client a tax advantage.

Supporting documents

3.19 For the most part, HMRC does not consider that it is necessary for a taxpayer to provide supporting documentation in order to satisfy the taxpayer's overriding need to make a correct return. HMRC's view is that, where it is necessary for that purpose, explanatory information should be entered in the 'white space' provided on the return. However, HMRC does recognise that the taxpayer may wish to supply further details of a particular computation or transaction in order to minimise the risk of a discovery assessment being raised at a later time.

3.20 Further HMRC guidance says that sending attachments with a tax return is intended for those cases where the taxpayer 'feels it is crucial to provide additional information to support the return but for some reason cannot utilise the white space'.

Approval of tax returns

3.21 It is essential that the member advises the client to review her tax return before it is submitted.

3.22 The member should draw the client's attention to the responsibility which the client is taking in approving the return as correct and complete. Attention should be drawn to any judgemental areas or positions reflected in the return to ensure that the client is aware of these and their implications before she approves the return.

3.23 A member should obtain evidence of the client's approval of the return in electronic or non-electronic form.

4. Tax advice

Introduction

4.1   Giving tax advice covers a variety of activities. It can involve advising a client on a choice afforded to her by legislation, for example, whether to establish a business as a sole trader, partnership or company. It could be advising on the tax implications of buying or selling an asset or business, or advising on succession planning.

4.2   For the most part clients are seeking advice on how to structure their affairs, either personal or commercial, in a way that is tax efficient and ensures that they comply with their legal and regulatory requirements. Transactions based on advice which are centred around non-tax objectives are less likely to attract scrutiny or criticism from stakeholders and are much more likely to withstand challenge by HMRC.

4.3   Some tax strategies have been the subject of heated public debate, raising ethical challenges. Involvement in certain arrangements could subject the client and the member to significantly greater compliance requirements, scrutiny or investigation as well as criticism from the media, government and other stakeholders and difficulties in obtaining professional indemnity insurance cover.

4.4   The definition of 'avoidance' is an evolving area that can depend on the tax legislation, the intention of Parliament, interpretations in case law and the varying perceptions of different stakeholders and is discussed further below.

4.5   A member should consider the contents of this Chapter carefully when giving tax advice and the potential negative impact of her actions on the public perception of the integrity of the tax profession more generally.

4.6   Clearly a member must never be knowingly involved in tax evasion, although, of course, it is appropriate to act for a client who is rectifying their affairs.

Tax planning vs tax avoidance?

4.7   Despite attempts by courts over the years to elucidate tax 'avoidance' and to distinguish this from acceptable tax planning or mitigation, there is no widely accepted definition.

4.8   Publicly, the term 'avoidance' is used in the context of a wide range of activities, be it multinational structuring or entering contrived tax-motivated schemes. The application of one word to a range of activities and behaviours oversimplifies the concept and has led to confusion.

4.9   In a 2012 paper on tax avoidance, the Oxford University Centre for Business Taxation states that transactions generally do not fall into clear categories of tax avoidance, mitigation or planning. Similarly, it is often not clear whether something is acceptable or unacceptable. Instead the paper concludes that there is:
'a continuum from transactions that would not be effective to save tax under the law as it stands at present to tax planning that would be accepted by revenue authorities and courts without question.'

Member's responsibility in giving tax planning advice

4.10   A member is required to act with professional competence and due care within the scope of her engagement letter.

5. Irregularities

Introduction

5.1 For the purposes of this Chapter, the term 'irregularity' is intended to include all errors whether the error is made by the client, the member, HMRC or any other party involved in a client's tax affairs.

5.2 In the course of a member's relationship with the client, the member may become aware of possible irregularities in the client's tax affairs. Unless already aware of the possible irregularities in question, the client should be informed as soon as the member has knowledge of them.

5.3 Where the irregularity has resulted in the client paying too much tax the member should advise the client about making a repayment claim and have regard to any relevant time limits. With the exception of this paragraph, the rest of this Chapter deals solely with situations where sums may be due to HMRC.

5.4 On occasion, it may be apparent that an error made by HMRC has meant that the client has not paid tax actually due or she has been incorrectly repaid tax. Correcting such mistakes may cause expense to a member and thereby to her clients. A member should bear in mind that, in some circumstances, clients or agents may be able to claim for additional professional costs incurred and compensation from HMRC.

5.5 A member must act correctly from the outset. A member should keep sufficient appropriate records of discussions and advice and when dealing with irregularities the member should:
- Give the client appropriate advice;
- If necessary, so long as she continues to act for the client, seek to persuade the client to behave correctly;
- Take care not to appear to be assisting a client to plan or commit any criminal offence or to conceal any offence which has been committed; and
- In appropriate situations, or where in doubt, discuss the client's situation with a colleague or an independent third party.

5.6 Once aware of a possible irregularity, a member must bear in mind the legislation on money laundering and the obligations and duties which this places upon him.

5.7 A member should also consider whether the irregularity could give rise to a circumstance requiring notification to her professional indemnity insurers.

5.8 In any situation where a member has concerns about her own position, she should take specialist legal advice. This might arise, for example, where a client appears to have used the member to assist in the commission of a criminal offence in such a way that doubt could arise as to whether the member had acted honestly and in good faith.

5.9 The irregularity steps flowchart (5.10) summarises the recommended steps a member should take where a possible irregularity arises.

4.11   A member should understand her client's expectations around tax advice or tax planning, and ensure that engagement letters reflect the member's role and responsibilities, including limitations in or amendments to that role. The importance of this has been highlighted by the Mehjoo case.

4.12   A member does not have to advise on or recommend tax planning which she does not consider to be appropriate or otherwise does not align with her own business principles and ethics. However, in this situation the member may need to ensure that the advice she does not wish to give is outside the scope of her engagement. If the member may owe a legal duty of care to the client to advise in this area, the member should ensure that she complies with this by, for example, advising the client that there are opportunities that the client could undertake, even though the member is unwilling to assist, and recommending that the client seeks alternative advice. Any such discussions should be well documented by the member.

4.13   Ultimately it is the client's decision as to what planning is appropriate having received advice and taking into account their own broader commercial objectives and ethical stance. However, the member should ensure that the client is made aware of the risks and rewards of any planning, including that there may be adverse reputational consequences. It is advisable to ensure that the basis for recommended tax planning is clearly identified in documentation.

4.14   Occasionally a client may advise a member that she intends to proceed with a tax planning arrangement without taking full advice from him on the relevant issues or despite the advice the member has given. In such cases the member should warn the client of the potential risks of proceeding without full advice and ensure that the restriction in the scope of the member's advice is recorded in writing.

4.15   Where a client wishes to pursue a claim for a tax advantage which the member feels has no sustainable basis the member should refer to Chapter 5 Irregularities for further guidance.

4.16   If Counsel's opinion is sought on the planning the member should consider including the question as to whether, in Counsel's view, the GAAR could apply to the transaction.

4.17   It should be noted that any legal opinion provided, for example by Counsel, will be based on the assumptions stated in the instructions for the opinion and on execution of the arrangement exactly as stated. HMRC and the courts will not be constrained by these assumptions.

The different roles of a Tax Adviser

4.18   A member may be involved in tax planning arrangements in the following ways:
- Advising on a planning arrangement.
- Introducing another adviser's planning arrangement.
- Providing a second opinion on a third party's planning arrangement.
- Compliance services in relation to a return which includes a planning arrangement.

A member should always make a record of any advice given.

5.10 Steps to take if there is a possible irregularity

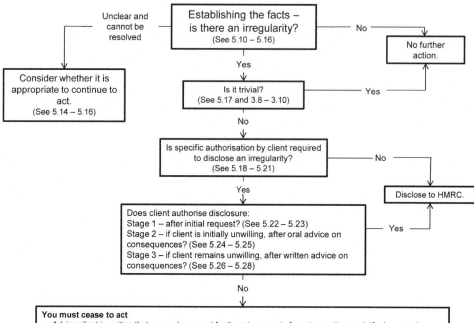

Establishing the facts –
is there an irregularity?
(See 5.10 – 5.16)

Unclear and
cannot be
resolved

No → No further action.

Consider whether it is
appropriate to continue to
act.
(See 5.14 – 5.16)

Yes

Is it trivial?
(See 5.17 and 3.8 – 3.10)

Yes → No further action.

No

Is specific authorisation by client required
to disclose an irregularity?
(See 5.18 – 5.21)

No → Disclose to HMRC.

Yes

Does client authorise disclosure:
Stage 1 – after initial request? (See 5.22 – 5.23)
Stage 2 – if client is initially unwilling, after oral advice on
consequences? (See 5.24 – 5.25)
Stage 3 – if client remains unwilling, after written advice on
consequences? (See 5.26 – 5.28)

Yes → Disclose to HMRC.

No

You must cease to act
- Advise client in writing that you no longer act for them in respect of any tax matters and, if relevant, other
  client matters. (See 5.29 – 5.31)
- Notify HMRC that you have ceased to act, if relevant. (See 5.32)
- Consider if you need to advise HMRC that any accounts/statements carrying a report signed by you can no
  longer be relied upon. (See 5.33 – 5.35)
- Consider whether a report should be made to MLRO/NCA. (See 5.36)
- Carefully consider your response to any professional enquiry letter. (See 5.37 – 5.39)

**At all times consider your obligations under anti-money laundering legislation and
whether you need to submit a Suspicious Activity Report.**

6. Access to data by HMRC

Introduction

6.1   For the purposes of this Chapter the term 'data' includes documents in whatever form (including electronic) and other information. While this guidance relates to HMRC requests, other government bodies or organisations may also approach the member for data. The same principles apply.

6.2   A distinction must be drawn between a request for data made informally and those requests for data which are made in exercise of a power to require the provision of the data requested ('statutory requests').

6.3   Similarly, requests addressed to a client and those addressed to a member require different handling.

6.4   Where a member no longer acts for a client, the member remains subject to the duty of confidentiality.

6.5   A member should comply with reasonable statutory requests and should not seek to frustrate legitimate requests for information. Adopting a constructive approach may help to resolve issues promptly and minimise costs to all parties.

6.6   Whilst a member should be aware of HMRC's powers in relation to the access, inspection and removal of data, given the complexity of the law relating to information powers, it may be appropriate to take specialist advice.

6.7   Revenue Scotland will have separate powers under the Revenue Scotland and Tax Powers Act 2014.

Informal requests addressed to the member

6.8   Disclosure in response to informal requests not made under any statutory power to demand data can only be made with the client's permission.

6.9   Sometimes the client will have authorised routine disclosure of relevant data, for example, through the engagement letter. However, if there is any doubt about whether the client has authorised disclosure or about the accuracy of details, the member should ask the client to approve what is to be disclosed.

6.10   Where an oral enquiry is made by HMRC, a member should consider asking for it to be put in writing so that a response may be agreed with the client.

6.11   Although there is no obligation to comply with an informal request in whole or in part, a member should advise the client whether it is in the client's best interests to disclose such data.

6.12   Informal requests may be forerunners to statutory requests compelling the disclosure of data. Consequently, it may be sensible to comply with such requests or to seek to persuade HMRC that a more limited request is appropriate. The member should advise the client as to the reasonableness of the informal request and likely consequences of not providing the data, so that the client can decide on her preferred course of action.

Informal requests addressed to the client

6.13 From time to time HMRC chooses to communicate directly with clients rather than with the appointed agent.

6.14 HMRC recognises the significant value which tax agents bring to both their clients and to the operation of the tax system. However, HMRC has also made it clear that on occasions it may deal with the taxpayer as well as, or instead of, the agent.

6.15 Examples of where HMRC may contact a member's client directly include:
- where HMRC is using 'nudge' techniques to encourage taxpayers or claimants to re-check their financial records or to change behaviour;
- where HMRC has become aware of particular assets, such as offshore investments, and the taxpayer is encouraged to consider whether a further tax disclosure is required;
- where the taxpayer has engaged in what HMRC considers to be a tax avoidance scheme, as HMRC considers that this will better ensure that the client fully understands HMRC's view.

6.16 HMRC has given reassurances that it is working to ensure that initial contact on compliance checks will normally be via the agent and only if the agent does not reply within an appropriate timescale will the contact be direct to the client.

6.17 When the member assists a client in dealing with such requests from HMRC, the member should apply the principles in 6.8 – 6.12.

Statutory requests addressed to the client

6.18 In advising the client a member should consider whether the notice is valid, how to comply with the request and the consequences of non-compliance. Specialist advice may be needed, for example on such issues as whether the notice has been issued in accordance with the relevant tax legislation, whether the data requested is validly included in the notice, legal professional privilege and human rights.

6.19 Even if the notice is not valid, in many cases the client may conclude that the practical answer is to comply. If the notice is legally effective the client is legally obliged to comply with the request.

6.20 The member should also advise the client about any relevant right of appeal against the statutory request if appropriate and of the consequences of a failure to comply.

Statutory requests addressed to the member

6.21 The same principles apply to statutory requests to the member as statutory requests to clients.

6.22 If a statutory request is valid it overrides the member's duty of confidentiality to her client.

6.23 In cases where the member is not legally precluded by the terms of the notice from communicating with the client, the member should advise the client of the notice and keep the client informed of progress and developments.

6.24 The member remains under a duty to preserve the confidentiality of her client, so care must be taken to ensure that in complying with any notice the member does not provide information or data outside the scope of the notice.

6.25   If a member is faced with a situation in which HMRC is seeking to enforce disclosure by the removal of data, the member should consider seeking immediate advice from a specialist adviser or other practitioner with relevant specialist knowledge, before permitting such removal, to ensure that this is the legally correct course of action.

6.26   Where a Schedule 36 notice is in point a member should note that it does not allow HMRC to inspect business premises occupied by a member in her capacity as an adviser. Specialist advice should be sought in any situation where HMRC asserts otherwise.

Privileged data

6.27   Legal privilege arises under common law and may only be overridden if this is expressly or necessarily implicitly set out in legislation. It protects a party's right to communicate in confidence with a legal adviser. The privilege belongs to the client and not to the member. If a document is privileged:
- The client cannot be required to make disclosure of that document to HMRC and a member should be careful to ensure that her reasons for advising a client nevertheless to make such a disclosure are recorded in writing.
- It must not be disclosed by any other party, including the member, without the client's express permission.

6.28   There are two types of legal privilege under common law, legal advice privilege covering documents passing between a client and her legal adviser prepared for the purposes of obtaining or giving legal advice and litigation privilege for data created for the dominant purpose of litigation. Litigation privilege may arise where litigation has not begun, but is merely contemplated and may apply to data prepared by non-lawyer advisers (including tax advisers) if brought into existence for the purposes of the litigation.

6.29   Communications from a tax adviser who is not a practising lawyer will not attract legal advice privilege but other similar protections exist under statute law, including:
- a privilege reporting exemption which applies to the reporting of money laundering in certain circumstances.
- a privilege under Schedule 36 whereby a tax adviser does not have to provide data that is her property and which constitute communications between the adviser and either her client or another tax adviser of the client. Information about such communications is similarly privileged. However, care should be taken as not all data may be privileged.

6.30   Whether data is or is not privileged and protected from the need to disclose is a complex issue, which will turn on the facts of the particular situation.

6.31   A member who receives a request for data, some of which she believes may be subject to privilege, should take independent legal advice on the position, unless expert in this area.

Reference Material

for AAT Assessment of Personal Tax

Finance Act 2016

Taxation tables for tasks 2-13

For assessments from 1 January – 31 December 2017

Note: this reference material is accessible by candidates during their live computer-based assessment for Personal Tax.

Reference material for AAT assessment of Personal Tax

Introduction
This document comprises data that you may need to consult during your Personal Tax computer-based assessment. The material can be consulted during the sample and live assessments through pop-up windows. It is made available here so you can familiarise yourself with the content before the test.

Do not take a print of this document into the exam room with you. Unless you need a printed version as part of reasonable adjustments for particular needs, in which case you must discuss this with your tutor at least six weeks before the assessment date.

This document may be changed to reflect periodical updates in the computer-based assessment, so please check you have the most recent version while studying. This version is based on Finance Act 2016 and is for use in AAT assessments 1 January – 31 December 2017.

Contents

Tax rates and bands

Rates	Bands	Normal rates (%)	Dividend rates (%)
Basic rate	£ 1 - £32,000	20	7.5
Higher rate	£32,001 - £150,000	40	32.5
Additional rate	£150,001 and over	45	38.1

Personal allowances

	£
Personal allowance	11,000
Savings allowance:	
• Basic rate taxpayer	1,000
• Higher rate taxpayer	500
Dividend allowance	5,000
Income limit for personal allowances	100,000

Individual savings accounts

	£
Annual limit	15,240

Car benefit percentage

	%
Emission for petrol engines:	
• 0g/km to 50g/km	7
• 51g/km to 75 g/km	11
• 76g/km to 94g/km	15
• 95g/km or more	16 + 1% for every extra 5g/km above 95g/km
Diesel engines	Additional 3%
Electric vehicles	7%

Car fuel benefit

	£
Base figure	22,200

Approved mileage allowance payments

Mileage	Payment
First 10,000 miles	45p per mile
Over 10,000 miles	25p per mile
Additional passengers (per passenger)	5p per mile
Motorcycles	24p per mile
Bicycles	20p per mile

Van scale charge

	£
Basic charge	3,170
Private fuel charge	598

	%
Benefit charge for zero emission vans	20

Non-taxable benefits

Staff party or event	£150 per head
Incidental overnight expenses:	
• Within the UK	£5 per night
• Overseas	£10 per night
Removal and relocation expenses	£8,000
Non-cash gifts from someone other than the employer	£250 per tax year
Staff suggestion scheme	Up to £5,000
Non-cash long service award	£50 per year of service
Work-related training courses	£15,480 per academic year
Health screening	1 per year
Mobile telephones	1 per employee
Childcare provision:	
• Basic rate taxpayer	£55 per week
• Higher rate taxpayer	£28 per week
• Additional rate taxpayer	£25 per week
Low-rate or interest free loans	Up to £10,000
Subsidised meals	£Nil
Provision of parking spaces	£Nil
Provision of workplace childcare	£Nil
Provision of workplace sports facilities	£Nil
Provision of eye tests and spectacles for VDU use	£Nil
Job-related accommodation	£Nil
Expensive accommodation limit	£75,000
Loan of assets annual charge	20%

HMRC official rate

HMRC official rate	**3%**

National Insurance contributions

	%
Class 1 Employee:	
• £1 to £8,060	0
• £8,061 to £43,000	12
• £43,001 and above	2
Class 1 Employer:	
• £1 to £8,112	0
• £8,113 and above	13.8
Class 1A	13.8

	£
Employment allowance	3,000

Capital gains tax and tax rates

Capital gains tax	£
Annual exempt amount	11,100
Tax rates	**%**
Basic rate	10
Higher rate	20

Inheritance tax – tax rates

	%
£1 to £325,000	0
Excess:	
• Death rate	40
• Lifetime rate	20

Inheritance tax – taper relief

	% reduction
3 years or less	0
Over 3 years but less than 4 years	20
Over 4 years but less than 5 years	40
Over 5 years but less than 6 years	60
Over 6 years but less than 7 years	80

Inheritance tax – exemptions

	£
Small gifts	250 per transferee per tax year
Marriage or civil partnership:	
• From parent	5,000
• From grandparent	2,500
• From one party to the other	2,500
• From others	1,000
Annual exemption	3,000

for your notes

for your notes

for your notes

for your notes

for your notes

for your notes